FERNS

of

THE TROPICS

WEE YEOW CHIN

Timber Press
Portland, Oregon

FERNS
of
THE TROPICS

Text and photographs © 1997 Times Editions Pte Ltd

Published in North America in 1998 by
Timber Press, Inc.
The Haseltine Building
133 S.W. Second Avenue, Suite 450
Portland, Oregon 97204, U.S.A.

Printed in Malaysia
ISBN 0-88192-458-X

CONTENTS

INTRODUCTION
7

PARTS OF A FERN
11

FERNS IN FOLKLORE AND SUPERSTITION
33

ECONOMIC USES OF FERNS
41

PROPAGATION OF FERNS
55

CULTIVATION OF FERNS
67

FERN HABITATS
73

FERN SPECIES
87

Glossary 178

Bibliography 180

Fern Societies 182

Acknowledgements 185

About the Author 186

Index 187

INTRODUCTION

The word "fern" comes from the old English *fearn*, which means feather. Why feather? Most people think of ferns as plants with lacy, delicate fronds, as their leaves are called. The fronds thus look very much like feathers. These are the ornamental ferns people cultivate in their gardens. But ferns do not always have "feathery" fronds. There are many with simple fronds, and unless examined closely, it is easy to mistake them for flowering plants. Fern fronds show much variation in shape and size. They are not always green. The newly emerging fronds of many species are brightly coloured, turning green only as they mature. There are also a few variegated ferns, specially selected for their horticultural attraction. Some ferns have coiled young fronds that look like fiddleheads, while others may be hooked, like a shepherd's crook.

Ferns belong to a group of non-flowering plants that includes algae, mosses and liverworts. They do not bear flowers and thus produce no fruits or seeds. Instead, they produce spores—thousands of them. Turn over a frond and it may be covered with brown spore sacs, or sporangia. Each sporangium is packed tight with microscopic brown spores. When mature, the dust-like spores are shed. Again, not all fern spores are brown or black—there are green and yellow spores as well.

Most people are familiar with horticultural ferns, especially the Maidenhair (*Adiantum*), Boston Fern (*Nephrolepis*), Staghorn (*Platycerium*) and Tree Fern (*Cyathea*). I am sure many are familiar with ferns as weeds, such as resam (*Dicranopteris*, *Gleichenia*), Climbing Fern (*Lygodium*) and Bracken Fern (*Pteridium aquilinum*). But I am not sure whether many people are aware that coal is composed almost entirely of fossilised ferns. During the Carboniferous period, some 350 million years ago, the earth was dominated by the ancestors of the present-day ferns and fern allies. Treelike Horsetails and Clubmosses up to 40 metres high towered above other large ferns. Giant Horsetails formed impenetrable thickets along river banks. Towards the end of this era, when the world's climate changed, these plants were replaced by the more competitive seed plants. The huge masses of ferns rotted away or become the coal seams of today. Strata of coal 50 centimetres deep consisting purely of fern spores have also been found.

Since then, many new fern species have evolved. Others have become extinct. Although there may have been many species that left no traces when they became extinct, the presence of a few is seen in fossils.

Just as the fronds of ferns come in different shapes and sizes, the plant itself comes in many forms. There are those that are as big as trees—the Tree Ferns of cool climates. At the other extreme there are the moss-like ferns of the wet tropical rainforest. While many ferns have their roots in the ground, there are just as many that grow on the branches of trees. These are called epiphytes. Epiphytic ferns do not harm the trees on which they grow; they only need a foothold on the branch or trunk. They make their own food rather than tapping nutrients from the host tree. There are others that grow from the ground and seek out a tree trunk to climb, to flourish at the crown of the tree where there is more light.

Ferns also vary in their demand for light. Shade ferns exist under the canopy of forest trees, while sun ferns grow and proliferate in the open, under the full glare of the tropical sun. Some even grow in deserts, although they seek the shelter of rocks to get away from the direct heat of the blazing sun. Water ferns, on the other hand, either grow on the surface of water or strike roots in the soil below the water. In fact, ferns are found in lowlands and mountains, in forests, in ponds, reservoirs and lakes, in freshwater and in salty mangrove swamps.

Once you become familiar with ferns, it is easy to recognise a fern. However, it is a little more difficult to identify a fern to its generic level or even to its specific level. Exceptions are seen in those with distinctive shapes, fronds or colours, making them easy to recognise.

Among the initiated, ferns are known by their scientific names. Groups of ferns with broad common characteristics are classified into families like Polypodiaceae and Ophioglossaceae, each ending with "aceae". Genera like *Platycerium*, *Pyrrosia* and *Lepisorus*, belonging to the family Polypodiaceae, have certain similar characteristics recognised by those who study ferns. Within a genus like *Platycerium* there are a number of species, which are distinguished by more defined characteristics like the type of nest and fronds, and the arrangement and location of the sporangia on the fronds. It is usual to write scientific names (genera and species) in italics to distinguish them from common names. Where a species has been referred to by its full name, such as *Platycerium coronarium*, subsequent references may be abbreviated for convenience to *P. coronarium*.

The importance of scientific names is obvious as they are standardised worldwide and in all languages. Thus a fern referred to by its scientific name (always latinised) should be understood by everyone, whatever his or her nationality or language. However, for everyday usage, ferns are given common names, and each country, region within a country, and language or dialect may have a different name or names for a specific fern. The common name "Staghorn" is understood almost everywhere, but other ferns may not be so obvious. And there are many ferns with no common names at all, as they have little or no economic importance.

Many monographs have been written on ferns, especially ferns of the United States, Australia, New Zealand, the United Kingdom and various other European countries. In Asia, where the fern flora is much richer, there are monographs on the ferns of Peninsular Malaysia, Thailand, Taiwan and the Philippines. These monographs are learned studies and are available for consultation by fern enthusiasts who are interested in the classification or the identification of less common species.

Within a species, especially among cultivated ferns, are different cultivars. Cultivars are horticultural variations within a species and are of more interest to horticulturists than to botanists. Fern cultivars can be genetically stable—that is, they can be grown true to type from spores or at least a percentage of the spores. These cultivars may be "sports"— variations that have arisen as a result of genetic mutation. Sports are relatively common among ferns. A batch of spores from a plant may give one or a few sporelings with a different frond shape or colour. These plants are readily recognised by fern enthusiasts and eagerly selected and propagated vegetatively. If they are popularly accepted by enthusiasts, they become a distinct cultivar of the species, usually abbreviated as "cv." after the species name. For example, there are a number of cultivars of the attractive Venus or true Maidenhair, *Adiantum capillus-veneris*, such as *A. capillus-veneris* cv. Fimbriatum. Hybridisation is another method of developing cultivars. For example, *A. capillus-veneris* cv. Mairisii is reported to be a hybrid between *A. capillus-veneris* and *A. cuneatum*. Other so-called cultivars may be just variations due to environmental conditions and may not be stable. There are a number of Bird's-nest Ferns with crested fronds that easily revert back to the uncrested form when exported to a country with different environmental conditions.

Worldwide, the number of fern species has been estimated to be more than 12,000. About half this number is believed to come from the wet tropics. In Peninsular Malaysia alone, where the fern flora has

been extensively studied, more than 500 native species have been recorded. This diversity can be appreciated if we compare it with the 54 species found in England, a country of similar land area. Or consider the African continent, which has a more than 200 times the land area but about the same number of species as Peninsular Malaysia. If the east Malaysian states of Sabah and Sarawak are taken into consideration, the fern flora of Malaysia can easily exceed 650 species. This is because the forests are much more extensive in Sabah and Sarawak, and within Sabah can be found Mt. Kinabalu, the highest mountain in Borneo.

PARTS OF A FERN

Except for the fact that they bear no flowers, ferns resemble flowering plants. They have a stem, leaves and roots. Only in tree ferns is the stem tall, looking like the trunk of a palm. In most cases the stem is short and erect. This is referred to as a rootstock. Many other stems are creeping; these are referred to as rhizomes. Some rhizomes are thin and wiry, others thick and short. Some grow along the ground while others grow underground. There are certain ferns which have developed thin rhizomes to help the plant climb up tree trunks and branches. Scales of different shapes or sometimes hairs cover the stem of ferns, affording some form of protection to the structure. Very often these are obvious on the young parts of the stem and fall off when the plant ages.

Embedded within the stem of the fern are numerous clumps of tiny conducting tubes, the vascular strands. These strands consist of xylem and phloem. Xylem transports water and mineral salts from the roots to the leaves, while phloem transports food materials from the leaves to all other parts of the plant.

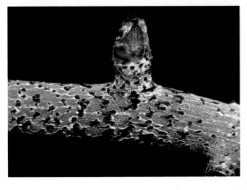

Opposite: **Platycerium coronarium**.

Top right: **Phymatorsorus scolopendria**.

Bottom right: A portion of the creeping rhizome of the epiphyte **Phymatosorus scolopendria** *covered with overlapping scales.*

11

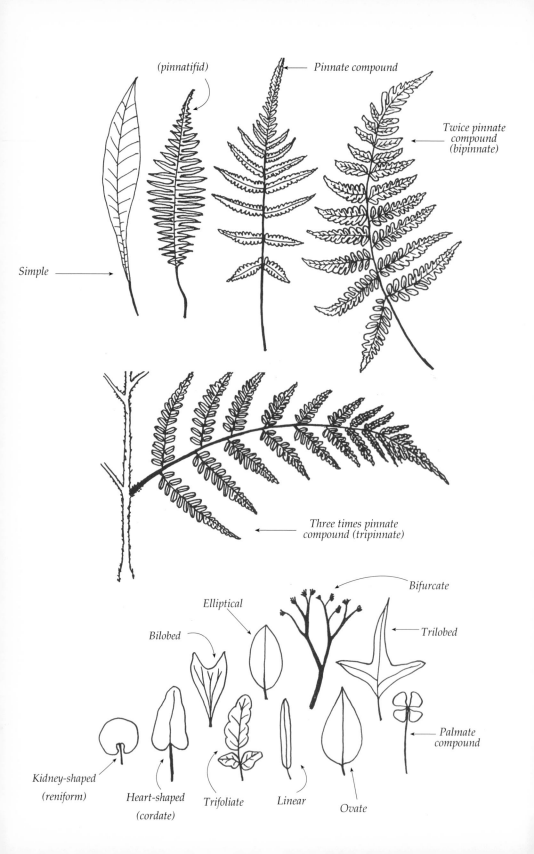

(pinnatifid)

Pinnate compound

Twice pinnate
compound
(bipinnate)

Simple

Three times pinnate
compound (tripinnate)

Bifurcate

Elliptical

Bilobed

Trilobed

Kidney-shaped
(reniform)

Heart-shaped
(cordate)

Trifoliate

Linear

Ovate

Palmate
compound

Fronds

The stem bears the fronds, which may be crowded at the tip of an upright stem or borne along the length of a creeping rhizome. Young fronds are typically coiled and are known as crosiers. As the young frond matures, the coiled tips unfold and the shape of the frond slowly becomes obvious. In a number of species the newly unfolded fronds are colourful, showing shades of pink, red or purple. Mature fronds may also show colours. The undersides of the fronds of the Silver Fern (*Pityrogramma calomelanos*) and the Gold Fern (*P. austroamericana*) are covered with waxy silver and gold powder respectively.

The fronds of a fern are equivalent to the leaves of a flowering plant. They are the most prominent part of a fern and are made up of a stalk, or stipe, bearing the frond blade, or lamina. Most stalks bear scales, hairs or even spines on the surface. The conducting tubes within the stalk join those in the stem to those in the frond blade. In simple fronds where the blade has an entire margin or where the blade is dissected into lobes, the so-called veins of the blade are actually extensions of the conducting tubes from the stalk as they divide and subdivide into smaller and smaller bundles in an effort to serve all the tissues of the blade.

However, not all fronds are simple in structure. Many ferns have dissected fronds where the blade is divided or even subdivided into many smaller divisions or lobes. Where the lobes are distinct and many make up a single frond, the frond is termed compound. If the frond is divided

*The base of the fern **Didymochlaena** sp. showing the stalks of old fronds and two young fronds still coiled in the form of crosiers. Note the presence of numerous reddish brown scales on the surface of the crosiers and the frond stalks.*

once and the divisions are arranged along the extension of the stalk, the frond is commonly termed pinnate compound and the divisions are known as pinnae. When the frond is divided twice, that is, the pinnae are divided into subdivisions called pinnules, the frond is twice pinnate compound or bipinnate. Such divisions can go on to three, four or even five times. Other fronds may be divided into lobes which are arranged like fingers on a palm. These fronds are termed palmate compound.

Most people are familiar with ferns with compound fronds. Ferns with simple fronds are not easily recognised as ferns unless other characteristics are examined. Simple fronds come in many different shapes, from oval to heart-shaped to kidney-shaped. Simple fronds may also be variously lobed, the lobes resembling the barbs of a feather or the fingers of a hand. Others may be lobed into pairs, with each of the two lobes further lobed into a pair. There are a number of species of ferns with two types of fronds, from slightly distinct to very distinct from each other. Staghorns (*Platycerium*) as well as a number of epiphytic ferns have normal foliage fronds, which become detached when they are old, and nest fronds, which remain on the plant even after they turn brown, to help trap leaf litter from the surrounding trees.

Opposite: A crosier of **Dipteris conjugata.**

Below: Young fronds of the **Centipede Fern (Blechnum orientale)** *are pinkish red.*

Opposite: The young, coppery brown fronds of **Stenochlaena palustris** *are eaten as a vegetable.*

Right: A star-like hair of **Platycerium coronarium** *from the surface of a young frond.*

Below (left): The silvery undersurface of the **Pityrogramma calomelanos** *frond is due to a coating of silvery wax.*

Below (right): The simple frond of **Tectaria singaporeana**, *covered with sori on the undersurface.*

Left: The large, hanging pinnate compound frond of **Goniophlebium percussum** *with the two rows of pinnae. The sori on the pinnae are also in two rows, on either side of the midrib. These are sunk in depressions on the undersurface, appearing as small lumps on the upper surface.*

Below left: The twice pinnate compound frond of **Cyathea latebrosa**. *The pinnae here are further subdivided into pinnules, each of which is shallowly lobed at the margin.*

Below right: The sterile and fertile fronds of **Stenochlaena palustris**. *Fertile fronds have narrower pinnae which are completely covered with sporangia.*

Opposite: The tripinnate compound frond of **Davallia denticulata**. *Only the lower pinnules are further subdivided, the upper ones being incompletely subdivided. There is no technical term for the final subdivisions of a tripinnate frond, which are usually also known as pinnules.*

Roots

The roots of the fern anchor the plant to the soil or help the rhizome attach itself to the branches and trunk of a tree. The roots are found at the base of the rootstock in an upright stem or along the entire length of a creeping rhizome. Among litter-collecting ferns like the Bird's-nest Fern (*Asplenium nidus*) and the Staghorn (*Platycerium*), the roots grow among the mass of decaying organic matter collected by the plant, holding it together as well as absorbing the nutrients when the organic matter breaks down. The roots of the Adder's-tongue Fern (*Ophioglossum*) harbour a fungus which lives in the cells. The spores of the Adder's-tongue Fern germinate in the dark and need the assistance of the fungus to obtain food for the young developing plant. Unless the right fungus is present and infects the first few roots emerging from the spore, the fern will not be able to survive its early stages. Only when the young plant emerges into the light can it survive on its own without the help of the fungus.

Sporangia

The reproductive structures of a fern— the sporangia, commonly called spore cases—are usually found clustered on the undersurface of the frond, although there are ferns that develop specialised out-growths for the purpose. Not all fronds bear sporangia. When the fern becomes reproductive, the newly developing fronds appear ready with young sporangia. As the frond matures, these sporangia mature with it. In a number of species, sterile fronds are distinctly different in shape or form from fertile fronds. Fertile fronds usually have a narrower blade or are bladeless.

Sporangia are usually clustered in distinct groups which may be round,

kidney-shaped, elongated along the veins or parallel to the midrib. These groupings of sporangia, or sori, can be unprotected or covered with an indusium, a membranous outgrowth from the frond. The indusium usually takes the shape of the grouping of sporangia. Thus a rounded sorus may have a rounded indusium and an elongated sorus an elongated indusium. The sporangia are found on the undersurface of the frond blade, and the indusium offers further protection to the sporangia, especially during the early stages of development. As the sporangia mature and increase in size, they outgrow the indusium, which then appears wrinkled and gradually dries up.

Sporangia are specialised structures consisting of a swollen portion one cell thick and a narrow stalk. Transversely encircling the swollen head of the sporangium is a single band of specialised cells, the annulus. These are dead cells with thick inner and thin outer walls and are much larger than the other cells of the sporangium. The annulus does not completely encircle the swollen head. It starts at the junction with the stalk, runs round the swollen head, and is interrupted towards the opposite end by a mass of thin-walled cells, the stomium. The stomium is the point of weakness of the sporangium. The annulus cells are filled

Opposite (top left): The young sori of **Nephrolepis biserrata**, *each totally covered with a kidney-shaped indusium.*

Opposite (top right): Maturing sori of **Nephrolepis biserrata** *with the indusia lifted up around the edge as the sporangia increase in size.*

Opposite (bottom): The marginal sori of **Adiantum sp.** *with their thin indusia.*

Below: The round sori of **Sphaerostephanos sp.** *with their hairy indusia.*

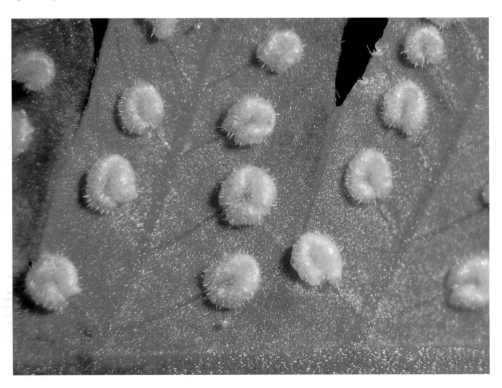

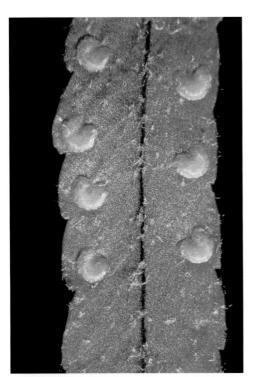

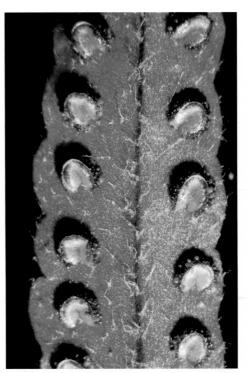

with water and as the air dries, this water evaporates, causing the annulus to straighten. This in turn applies pressure to the stomium. With further drying of the annular cells, the sporangium suddenly ruptures and its upper half, together with the spores, is flung back. Just as suddenly, it returns to its original position. These two movements effectively catapult the spores out of the case into the surroundings, to be dispersed by the air current. This process of spore dispersal can be observed under a microscope or a hand lens with a table lamp providing the external heat.

Right: Sori on the undersurface of a pinnule of **Pityrogramma calomelanos**. *Each sorus is made up of a number of young green and old black sporangia. The brown band going round the swollen head of each sporangium is the annulus.*

Below: Maturing sporangia of **Pteris vittata**, *each with a prominent band, the annulus, circling the swollen head.*

Spores

Each sporangium is usually packed with 64 tiny spores in groups of four known as tetrads. Just before the spores are shed, the tetrads separate. These spores are the reproductive structures of the fern. They are bean-shaped or shaped like a three-sided pyramid and are microscopic, with the surface either plain or variously sculptured.

Spores are very different from seeds. A seed is a sort of miniature plant packed with food reserves to tide over its early stages of life. A spore is a simple, one-celled structure with very limited food reserves, if any at all. Spores sacrifice food reserves for mobility and can be carried long distances by the wind. However, spores are vulnerable to environmental conditions. Thus, the ability of ferns to establish in new grounds is not limited by distance but by the ability of their spores to survive the periods of transportation, germination, and subsequent growth and fertilisation. If a spore falls on a moist surface, it will germinate. If conditions continue to be shaded and moist, it will survive the early stages after germination. These conditions must be maintained for the next few weeks if a new fern is to develop, for during its early life it is extremely vulnerable to drying.

Below left: Spores of **Dicranopteris linearis**, *each with a tri-radiate thickening, marking the point of contact of the original four spores before they are separated.*

Below right: Spores of **Ophioglossum nudicaule** *(top) and* **Pyrrosia piloselloides** *(bottom) under the scanning electron microscope, showing the surface ornamentation.*

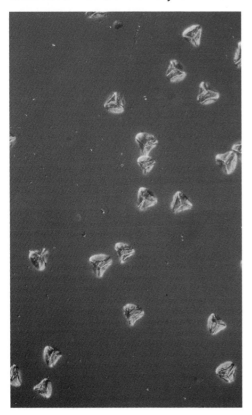

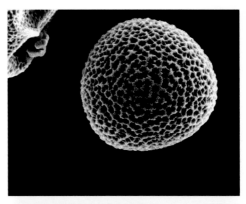

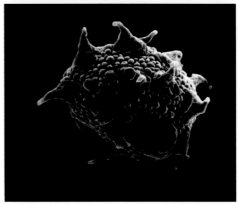

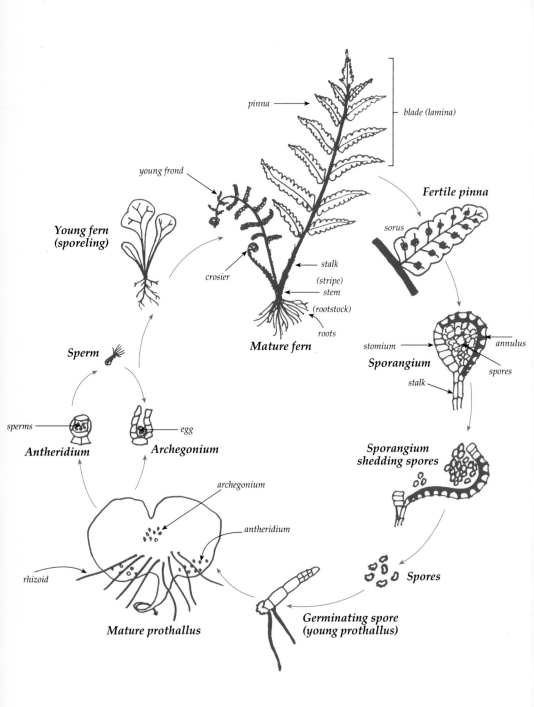

pinna → ... → blade (lamina)

young frond

Young fern (sporeling)

crosier

Fertile pinna

sorus

stalk (stripe)
stem (rootstock)
roots

Mature fern

Sperm

stomium → ... → annulus
spores

Sporangium

stalk

sperms → *Antheridium*

egg → *Archegonium*

Sporangium shedding spores

archegonium

antheridium

rhizoid

Spores

Mature prothallus

Germinating spore (young prothallus)

The Life Cycle of a Fern

THE LIFE CYCLE OF A FERN

A fern has two phases in its life cycle. On germination, the spore develops into a heart-shaped structure called a prothallus, which is usually not more than 5 mm across. This is the sexual phase of the fern's life cycle, and is not normally obvious. The central cushion of the prothallus is many cells thick and bears numerous, brown, threadlike rhizoids. Rhizoids function like roots, absorbing water and nutrients for the growing prothallus. The major portion of the prothallus consists of a pair of one-cell-thick wings on both sides of the central cushion.

During its growing period, which may take from one to several weeks, sexual organs develop on the underside of the prothallus. Male organs, the antheridia, are simple oval structures bearing sperms. Female organs, the archegonia, are flask-shaped with the swollen end containing an egg. Whether male, female, or both types of sexual organs develop during this period depends on many factors. Only when both sexual organs are present and they mature in unison can the sperms from the antheridium fertilise the egg in the archegonium. The sperms require the presence of a film of water on the undersurface of the prothallus to travel to an archegonium and enter its neck to reach the egg. They are guided to the egg by chemicals released from the maturing archegonium.

Once a sperm fertilises the egg, the egg develops into an embryo, which in turn gives rise to a young sporeling. The first frond of the sporeling is a simple, narrow structure, very different from the frond of the adult plant. Subsequent fronds become more and more dissected until they finally take the form of the adult structure. The sporeling develops its own roots and

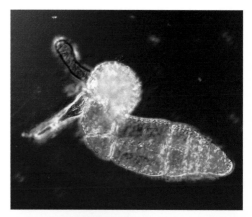

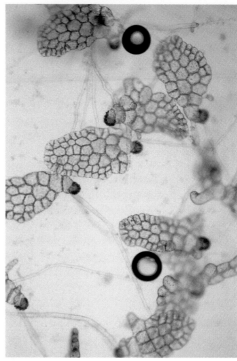

*Top: An early phase in the germination of a **fern spore.** Two rhizoids have developed together with a many-celled germ tube, the tip of which is actively dividing.*

*Bottom: Young **prothalli** just before the heart-shaped stage. The spores are still obvious as roundish dark structures. Each prothallus has a number of long, thin rhizoids which are one-celled and light brown. The prothalli are many-celled and green, packed with chloroplasts. (The two dark rings at the top and bottom of the picture are air bubbles).*

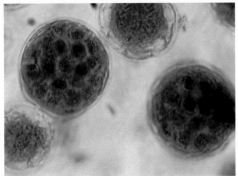

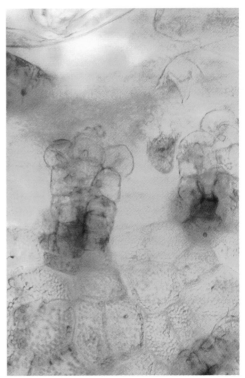

becomes independent of the prothallus, after which the prothallus withers and dies. The sporeling or young fern represents the prominent or asexual phase of the fern's life cycle. With maturity, the fern plant bears asexual spores which in turn germinate to begin the sexual phase.

There are a few ferns, especially water ferns (*Azolla*, *Salvinia*, and *Marsilea*) that produce two types of spores. The smaller male spores develop into prothalli bearing antheridia, while the bigger female spores develop into prothalli bearing only archegonia. The two types of prothalli must be located very close to each other before fertilisation can occur.

The sexual phase of the fern is the weak link in its life cycle, and many factors can end the fern's further development. The delicate nature of the prothallus makes

*Above left (top): A heart-shaped fern **prothallus** with many round antheridia, the male sex organs.*

*Above left (bottom): **Antheridia** packed with developing sperms.*

*Above right: Close-up of the female sex organs, the **archegonia**, with the top of the neck opened to receive the sperms.*

it highly vulnerable to drying conditions, as moisture is easily lost from its surface, drying it permanently. Timing is also important; unless both types of sexual organs are present and mature at the same time, successful fertilisation will not be possible. Another important factor is the presence of moisture at the time of fertilisation to enable the movement of the sperms. The necessity of millions of spores to ensure the successful development of a single sporeling is therefore obvious.

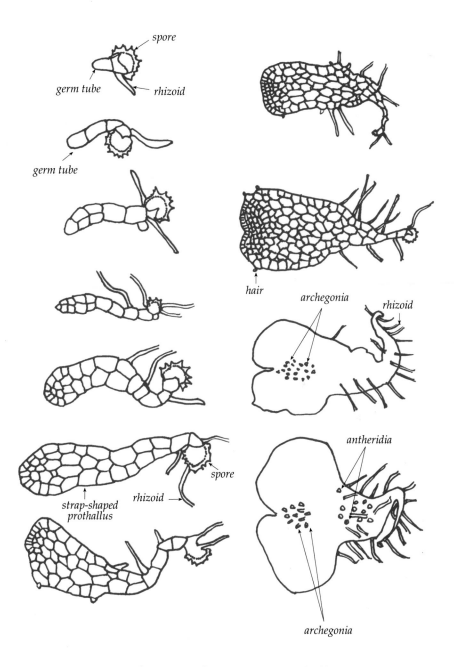

Development of Spore into Prothallus

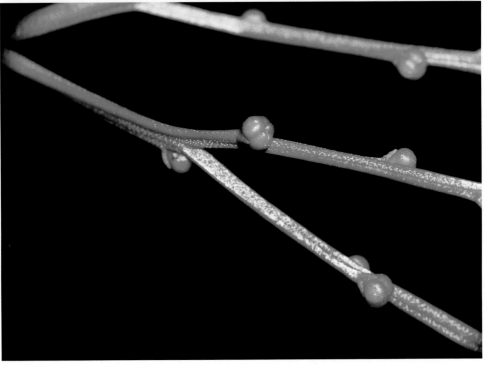

FERN ALLIES

The Whisk Fern (*Psilotum*), Clubmoss (*Lycopodium*), Spikemoss (*Selaginella*) and Horsetail (*Equisetum*) are a special group of plants which are closely related to true ferns but at the same time have distinctively different characteristics. For one, fern allies do not possess distinct fronds but instead have small leaves known as microphylls. These microphylls have a single vein each and are arranged along simple or branched stems. Sporangia are present, but these are borne in the axils of microphylls, arranged in cones at the tips of branches. Sporangia are never found on the undersurface of microphylls. Spores may be of one type only or of two types. Fern allies with single type spores, such as *Psilotum* and *Lycopodium*, produce one type of prothalli which bear both the male and female organs. Those with two types of spores, such as certain species of *Selaginella*, produce separate male and female prothalli bearing either male or female reproductive organs.

Opposite (top): The **Whisk Fern** **(Psilotum nudum)** *bears a clump of green, wiry stems with much reduced leaves at intervals. Sporangia are relatively large; three are fused into a bigger structure and appear together with the leaves. The fleshy rhizome is underground, harbouring a fungus which assists it in obtaining nutrients. The plant in this picture grows from the base of a tree together with the fern* Pyrrosia. *Note the thin, green stem showing paired branching.*

Opposite (bottom): Close-up of branches of **Psilotum** **nudum** *with fused sporangial structures.*

Below: **Clubmoss** **(Lycopodium cernuum)** *is a many-branched plant with a slender stem covered with small leaves (microphylls), which appear as short, green projections. The fertile cone at the end of the branches bears sporangia at the base of fertile leaves.*

Left: **Lycopodium cernuum** *branches with spirally arranged microphylls and fertile cones at the tips.*

Right: The **Horsetail** *(***Equisetum***) with its erect, green aerial stems. The leaves are much reduced in size and fused, occurring at intervals in whorls around the stem. The aerial stem contains granules of silica, making it valuable for use as an abrasive in the polishing of wood and the cleaning of pots. The picture here shows* Equisetum hyemale *at the Botanical Gardens in Tokyo.*

Below: **Spikemoss (***Selaginella***)** *is another group of fern allies. It is recognised by the presence of two types of leaves—two rows of small, normal leaves along the stem and another two rows of smaller leaves found inside the larger pairs. This plant has developed a blue sheen as a result of growing in deep shade. Under lighter shade, plants generally appear green. The Malay names for this plant give an indication of its gracefulness and beauty—paku merak (peacock's fern),* jambu merak *(peacock's crest) and* ekor merak *(peacock's tail).*

FERNS IN FOLKLORE AND SUPERSTITION

Ferns do not have flowers and they produce no seeds. They reproduce by releasing microscopic spores, but this was not known before the 16th century. The ability of ferns to sprout all over the place without any visible seeds convinced people that these plants had seeds, but that they must be invisible. Is it a wonder then that superstitions and myths became associated with ferns, and magical powers were ascribed to them? Many believed that those who had such seeds in their possession had the power to make themselves invisible. Even during Shakespeare's time this belief was evident, as seen in the following lines from Henry IV (Part I, Act II, Scene I):

Gadshill: We have the receipt of fern-seed,
　　　we walk invisible.
Chamberlain: Nay, by my faith, I think you are more
　　　beholding to the night
　　　than to fern-seed for your walking invisible.

There is an old English belief that on July 24, which is St John's Eve, ferns develop pale blue flowers which turn to shining golden seeds to ripen at midnight.

*A vertical colony of the **Disc Staghorn** on a terentang tree in the Bukit Timah Nature Reserve in Singapore. Older Malays believe that this plant houses the ghost of a woman who died in childbirth.*

Believers spread cloth beneath the ferns and, to the accompaniment of incantations and prayers, waited to collect the seeds. They must have been disappointed, and fairies must have been blamed for stealing the seeds! Others placed 12 pewter plates beneath the plant. The magical seeds were supposed to fall through 11 plates to rest on the twelfth. This practice was forbidden by the church in the 16th century, but it continued as late as the 19th century. Russians also observed this ritual on St John's Eve. They believed that those fortunate enough to possess the flower or even view it would become rich, either through having their wishes granted or by finding buried treasures.

According to an old legend, ferns did bear flowers once upon a time. However, at the time of the birth of Christ, when all the other plants that made up the straw in the stable put forth flowers in honour of the event, only the ferns failed to do so. As a punishment, ferns were thereafter condemned to being flowerless.

Biting a fern seed or the first unfolding frond was believed by many to guarantee one against toothache for an entire year. To put a curse on a person, you need only to blow the "dust" of the Horsetail towards the person while uttering the relevant curse.

*The apical portions of the **Golden Chicken Fern** (Cibotium barometz) for sale in Padang, Sumatra.*

Fern fronds were similarly associated with myths and superstitions. People believed that ferns had the power to drive away evil and to protect one from magical spells. Many people kept fiddleheads, which were known as St John's Hands, in their houses or even on their person to keep evil spirits at bay. Fronds were hung over doors to keep lightning away, and in fact the English used to grow Bracken (*Pteridium aquilinum*) on the roof of their houses as protection against thunder and lightning. Burning Bracken was thought to have some influence on the local rainfall. Whenever the king of England was scheduled to go hunting, farmers were ordered not to burn Bracken. The English used the stalks of this fern as charms, to ward off evil spirits. This was because the pattern of the vascular tissue resembles the letter C, Christ's initial, when the stem is cut across. The Scots saw the vascular marking as that of the devil's hoof. On the other hand, the Irish called it the Fern of God, as in sectioning the stem, the cross-section appears first as G, then O and finally D.

Travellers to Central Europe and Asia in the 1700s brought back strange stories of a charm in the shape of a lamb. Not knowing whether it was of animal or plant origin, they invoked the legend of the Tartarian or Scythian Lamb. This animal, according to legend, was tied to one spot and took to growing roots and eating air. The so-called lamb is actually the apical portion of the Golden Chicken Fern (*Cibotium barometz*), including the young fiddleheads covered with masses of fine golden hairs. These charms were hung in houses to ward off evil.

Such pieces are still being sold in Taiwan, the Philippines and Malaysia as charms. In the 1970s, when the forests of the Genting Highlands in Peninsular Malaysia were being cleared for the construction of the hotel-casino complex, many such tree ferns became accessible to collectors, who then lopped off their apices and sold them in pots as Golden Chicken Plants, to be used as table ornaments and charms. The vendors went so far as to claim that these "plants" could bring many benefits to owners, from keeping the house cool and warding off evil to curing certain illnesses. The golden hairs were used centuries ago in China as a styptic (a substance for contracting blood vessels). The dried rhizomes covered with hairs were regularly exported from the Malay Peninsular to China, reaching Europe via Russia in 1772.

The fertile leaf of the Adder's-tongue Fern (*Ophioglossum*) resembles the head of a snake with a protruding tongue. Thus, people believed that the fern had great powers for evil, and that the fern would destroy the grass around it and injure cattle which grazed upon it. This fern is also used as a cure for snake bites. In certain parts of rural Britain, a traditional

*The frond of the tropical **Bracken** (Pteridium caudatum), which is very similar to the temperate P. aquilinum, showing the paired pinna branches.*

remedy called Adder's Spear Ointment is available for use in the treatment of sore eyes and snake bites. This ointment is made from the leaves of *Ophioglossum vulgatum* infused or boiled in the oil of unripe olives and set in the sun for a number of days. Adder's-tongue and Moonwort were both part of the pharmacopoeia of medieval European witches, together with such poisonous and hallucinogenic herbs as hemlock, henbane, mandrake and deadly nightshade.

The Moonwort (*Botrychium lunaria*) is a small fleshy plant with leafy lobes that look like miniature bunches of grapes. It was much respected in medieval Europe as it was believed to have the power to open any lock and to unshoe any horse that stepped on it. Alchemists sought it for its supposed power to change quicksilver (mercury) into real silver. When the pinnae are spread out they look like saddles, hence

the old belief that the fronds were used by little fairies to saddle their equally little horses.

The Maidenhair Fern (*Adiantum capillus-veneris*), with its slender stalks and delicate fronds, was believed to be the hair of Venus, goddess of love and beauty. This belief was based on the quality of the fronds, which take on a silvery sheen when placed under water and remain perfectly dry when removed. In Roman times, a potion made from the fern was supposed to give grace, beauty and love. The fronds, together with wild celery, oil and wine, were used to treat baldness or to give a thick growth of hair.

The underground stem of the Male Fern (*Dryopteris filix-mas*) was an essential ingredient in love potions. Gently applied onto the eyelids of a sleeping person, it was supposed to make the person fall in love with the first person of the opposite

sex he or she sees on waking up. The rhizomes were dug up at midsummer, dried over the smoke of a fire and fashioned into the shape of human hands. These shrivelled structures were known as Dead Man's Hands or St John's Hands and were carried as charms against witches and evil spirits. This belief was reinforced by the cross-section of the structure when cut, which shows the marking of a cross.

Older Malays believe that the Disc Staghorn Fern (*Platycerium coronarium*) houses the ghost of a woman who died in childbirth. The Malays call it *paku langsuyur*, *rumah langsuyur* or *semun bidadari* (*bidadari* means fairy, nymph, angel or a beautiful woman). The *langsuyur* is a Malay vampire generated by the malevolence of a woman dying in child-birth. It was believed that the vampire seeks out pregnant women for their blood or the blood of the newborn infant. It was supposed to take the form of a beautiful maiden with long hair that rustles as she flies in the dark to alight on a tall tree or in the nest of the Staghorn Fern or Bird's-nest Fern. Some people believed that the *langsuyur* could also take the form of a beautiful woman with a hole in her neck. Thus, to prevent a woman who died in childbirth from becoming such a vampire, glass beads were put in the corpse's mouth to keep her from shrieking; hen's eggs were laid under her armpits so that she would not lift them to fly; and needles were placed in the palms of her hands so that she might not open and clench them to assist her flight.

Many species of ferns have been put to use in folk medicine. Women in the Moluccas shred the leaves of *Ophioglossum pendulum* and soak them in oil to be used to improve the appearance of their hair. The lovely strands of leaves dangling from the nest of the Staghorn Fern, appearing like so many strands of hair, obviously suggest this usage. The leaves of the Grass Fern (*Schizaea digitata*) are narrow and erect, like tufts of grass pointing upwards, hence its reputation as an aphrodisiac among the Malays. The elongated leaves of the Spleenwort (*Asplenium*) resemble the spleen, so these plants are used against illnesses of the spleen. The Horsetail

Left: **Adder's-tongue Fern (Ophioglossum nudicaule)** *growing in the garden of a house in Singapore.*

Opposite (top): The unfernlike **Moonwort (Botrychium sp.)** *with its erect branched spikes laden with large, round sporangia.*

Opposite (bottom): A lush display of the **Maidenhair Fern (Adiantum sp.)** *at the Kandy Botanic Gardens in Sri Lanka.*

(*Equisetum*), with its jointed stems, is used to treat pain in the joints. The American Cherokee Indians used the fiddleheads of ferns to treat rheumatism and heart problems—as the fiddleheads unfurled, so would they impart such "uncurling properties" to the arthritic or rheumatic limbs, as well as relieving problems resulting from the lungs wrapping round the heart.

Opposite: An old nest of the **Disc Staghorn Fern** *infested with the* **Hanging Adder's-tongue Fern** (**Ophioglossum pendulum**)*, with many ribbon-like fronds dangling from the nest.*

Above: The **Male Fern** (**Dryopteris filix-mas**)*.*

Right: The **Grass Fern** (**Schizaea digitata**) *is very common in old rubber plantations, growing under the shade of the rubber canopy. The erect grassy fronds are easily overlooked until the brown apical tufts of sori are noticed.*

ECONOMIC USES OF FERNS

Ferns are often thought of as rather attractive plants with limited economic uses. At best, they serve as ornamental plants and at worst, they are weeds that need to be eradicated. This may be true in urban societies where our every need can be obtained, at a price, from the local supermarket. However, in rural communities where agriculture plays a major role in everyday life, the usefulness of ferns is much more appreciated. Besides binding the soil on which they grow and thus helping to control erosion, ferns provide food, medicine and construction materials, as well as materials for use in decorative and ritualistic items.

FOOD

Starch has been obtained from the woody stem of Tree Ferns (*Cyathea* spp.) and the fleshy rootstock and frond bases of giant ferns like *Angiopteris* and *Marattia*. However, as it can only be obtained in small amounts and it is not very palatable, fern starch is only eaten during times of serious food shortage. In the past, such starch was eaten in India, New Zealand,

the Philippines, Madagascar, New Guinea, New Caledonia, Hawaii and Australia. The Australian aborigines collected the rhizomes of *Blechnum indicum* as well as the sporocarps of *Marsilea* and ground them to obtain starch, which they made into a kind of unleavened bread. In Hawaii, the starchy hearts of Tree Ferns are fed to pigs during times of famine. During the early part of this century, laundry starch was extracted from the pith of Tree Fern trunks.

The young fronds or fiddleheads of many ferns are eaten as greens. There are many species of ferns in the tropics whose fiddleheads are regularly collected and eaten raw, cooked, preserved in brine, or pickled. These include the Swamp Fern (*Acrostichum aureum*), Centipede Fern (*Blechnum orientale*), Tree Fern (*Cyathea contaminans*), Ladder Fern (*Nephrolepis hirsutula*), Spider Brake (*Pteris multifida*) and Climbing Fern (*Stenochlaena palustris*). *Diplazium esculentum* is reportedly the most popular because it is the tastiest of them all. Bundles of freshly uncurled fronds are a common sight in the rural markets of the Philippines, Indonesia, Malaysia and New Guinea. Some restaurants even offer this fern as an exotic vegetable dish, when supplies are available.

Carvings of **Tree Fern** *stems in a private garden in Bogor, Indonesia*

The entire plant of the Horned Fern (*Ceratopteris thalictroides*, or in Malay, *sayur kodok* or frog's vegetable) and the young shoots of the Elephant Fern (*Angiopteris evecta*) are eaten as a vegetable, while *tunjuk langit* (*Helminthostachys zeylanica*) makes an excellent green vegetable. The emerging shoots of Male Fern (*Dryopteris filix-mas*) are boiled and eaten as a kind of asparagus in Norway. The shoots of the Horsetail (*Equisetum arvense*) were once eaten extensively by the Romans and North American Indians. In Nepal the tubers of *Nephrolepis cordifolia* are eaten after roasting.

Fiddleheads of the Ostrich Fern (*Matteuccia struthiopteris*) are regarded as a delicacy and are commercially exploited in the United States. They taste like asparagus and are sold fresh, frozen or canned. They are eaten in salads, cooked as a vegetable, added to soups or made into soufflés. The fiddleheads of the Royal Fern (*Osmunda regalis*) and the Bracken (*Pteridium*) are similarly eaten fresh in Japan and Korea. The former is also eaten in the Philippines, the United States, Europe and New Zealand. These freshly picked fiddleheads of Bracken are first immersed briefly in boiling water containing a little wood ash or sodium bicarbonate. This removes the bitterness of the shoots, which are then boiled in plain water and flavoured with fish powder and soy sauce prior to eating. They may be preserved in salt solution or dried.

Bracken rhizomes and fronds have been eaten in many countries, and there are 19th-century records of powdered rhizomes being used as bread-making flour in New Zealand, the Canary Islands, France and Britain. When food was in short supply during World War I, Bracken rhizomes were recommended as food. Roasted rhizomes are still sometimes eaten in Scotland, while in New Zealand the Maoris roast the rhizomes in ash before eating. Young Bracken shoots have been recommended as a substitute for asparagus in England, France and particularly Japan, where they are regarded as a delicacy and eaten fresh, dried or pickled.

People have long known that Bracken poisons livestock, but it is only in recent years that evidence has emerged that the plant has carcinogenic properties. Still,

Left: A young frond of **Cyathea contaminans** *standing erect with the pinnae uncurling and the pinnules still curled up.*

Opposite (top): The crosier of the **Centipede Fern (Blechnum orientale).**

Opposite (bottom): The **Horned Fern (Ceratopteris thalictroides)** *or in Malay,* sayur kodok *or frog's vegetable. The narrowly lobed fronds of this water fern are eaten as a vegetable.*

the Japanese continue to consume the shoots, believing that the traditional way of preparing the shoots with ash helps remove the cancer-producing toxins, or at least reduce their levels significantly. The relatively high rate of stomach cancer among the Japanese may, in fact, be due to the high consumption of these shoots.

Livestock poisoning as a result of animals grazing on the young fronds and rhizomes of Bracken is a worldwide problem. Horses and pigs suffer from "Bracken staggers" while cattle and sheep may become blind. Low consumption of Bracken by these animals over a long period may result in tumours.

The carcinogenic properties of Bracken have in fact been demonstrated in a

number of experiments with animals (quail, guinea pigs, mice, cows, sheep) where malignant tumours developed as a result of its consumption. There is also evidence to suggest that the carcinogenic factor may be transmitted to humans through the consumption of milk and dairy products of cows that have grazed on Bracken. People living in areas overgrown with Bracken and constantly exposed to air containing Bracken spores may be in danger of developing cancer as a consequence.

BEVERAGES

Many ferns are brewed into a variety of beverages. The rhizomes of Male Fern (*Dryopteris filix-mas*) and Bracken Fern (*Pteridium*) are sometimes substituted for hops in the brewing of beer in Europe. The

Fiddleheads of the **Ostrich Fern (Matteuccia struthiopteris)** *taste like asparagus and are commercially exploited in the United States.*

dried fronds of the Maidenhair Fern (*Adiantum pedatum*) are supposed to make a fine tea, and the pleasant-tasting Bavarian tea, which is a mixture of ordinary tea, *Adiantum capillus-veneris* and milk, is claimed to have the property of inducing perspiration. The side branches of Horsetail (*Equisetum arvense*) are made into "shave grass tea". In Costa Rica, tea brewed from the Giant Horsetail (*Equisetum giganteum*) is widely consumed to treat kidney diseases. In India, *Angiopteris* stem is fermented into an intoxicating drink.

MEDICINE

Various European, American, Asian and African cultures have made use of ferns in their traditional medicines to cure ailments from rheumatism, bowel disorders, burns, sprains and ulcers to bites and stings. The fronds, rhizomes or roots are pounded and applied externally, or made into a decoction, either by themselves or with other herbs, and taken internally. For example, the pounded fronds of the Maidenhair *Adiantum capillus-veneris* is applied to snake bites in Taiwan; *Drynaria rigidula* has been used to treat venereal diseases in Malaysia; an extract of *Asplenium trichomanes* soaked in wine is used to treat lumbago in China; and the pounded rhizomes of *Drynaria sparsisora* are applied externally to reduce swollen limbs and boils in Indonesia. The list is endless.

In many cases, these cultures have been led to believe in the curative properties of ferns because of the unique appearance of the plant or parts of the plant. The use of the Adder's-tongue Fern (*Ophioglossum*) to treat snake bites is a good example. Another example is the use by the Chinese of the Spikemoss, *Selaginella involvens*, to treat various problems related to old age.

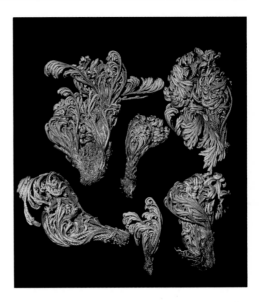

The dried **Selaginella involvens**, *a much sought-after Chinese medicinal herb.*

These plants curl up under dry conditions and uncurl when moisture is available. This behaviour of "dying and yet not dying" must have inspired the Chinese to make use of the plant for such a purpose.

The use of ferns to expel parasitic worms is practised worldwide, from China and India to Africa, Europe and North America. This practise dates back to at least 300 BC, when the Greek botanist and physician Theophrastus recommended an oil extract of fern for such a purpose. Fronds of *Cyathea mannjana* and *Dryopteris cristata*; spores of *Lycopodium selago*; and rhizomes of *Acrostichum aureum*, *Blechnum orientale*, *Drynaria quercifolia*, and *Pteridium aquilinum* have been used. In fact the rhizomes and stipes of the European Male Fern (*Dryopteris filix-mas*) and Marginal Fern (*D. marginalis*) have been shown to contain an oleoresin that effectively expels tapeworms from the intestine. These species have been employed for centuries by people from North America, Europe and Asia to expel intestinal worms. Various other species of *Dryopteris* have also been used in Japan and China.

The diuretic properties of ferns such as *Adiantum macrophyllum*, *Blechnum orientale*, *Lecanopteris carnosa*, *Lycopodium clavatum* and *Microsorum punctatum* have been put to good use in treating swellings. *Lycopodium macrophyllum* and *Pteris ensiformis* have been used to treat dysentery, while *Psilotum nudum* is reputed to have laxative properties.

Adiantum capillus-veneris, *Dicranopteris linearis* and *Nephrolepis cordifolia* have been used for chest complaints. *Angiopteris evecta* and *Lycopodium cernuum* have been used for rheumatism. Many species are used to treat boils, ulcers and wounds. These include *Dicranopteris linearis*, *Pteris ensiformis*, *Pityrogramma calomelanos* and *Adiantum flabellulatum*.

The Chinese have long used the Horsetail *Equisetum hyemale* to treat the liver and the eye. The plant is astringent, antihaemorrhagic, diuretic and diaphoretic. In Indonesia it is used to treat bruises, fractures and arthritis. The Chinese have recently conducted clinical trials to show its effectiveness in treating acute infectious hepatitis.

FERTILISER

The Mosquito Fern (*Azolla pinnata*) is so called because its presence on the water surface prevents mosquitoes from breeding. This fern is used extensively in Southeast Asian countries as a green manure, especially in rice farming. During the early stage of cultivation when the fields are flooded, the presence of this fern, together with the blue-green alga *Anabaena azollae* found within the lower lobe of the frond, helps enrich the soil as the alga fixes free nitrogen. As the crop matures, the fern serves as a green manure for the drying rice fields.

EROSION CONTROL

In the tropics, pure thickets of *Dicranopteris* and *Gleichenia* colonise degraded land. Although these thickets of ferns keep other plants from growing in the area and maintain their purity for decades, they have a function in preventing soil erosion. These ferns can effectively be eradicated through fire as their rhizomes grow on the soil surface. However, the Bracken Fern (*Pteridium*) spreads by underground rhizomes and fires only help maintain the purity of the fern. However, regular firing of the thicket can destroy it. This fern has been used in Australia to stabilise coastal areas. In New Zealand, *Dicksonia squarrosa* has been used to stabilise roadside cuttings.

ORNAMENTAL USES

Fern fronds are widely used in flower bouquets and flower arrangements because of their lacy appearance. A modern usage is to freeze-dry fronds and paint them gold or silver for use in dried flower arrangements. Ferns also make attractive potted plants, especially the many species and cultivars of the *Adiantum*, *Nephrolepis*, *Pteris* and *Davallia*. In Singapore, Indonesia and Thailand, Staghorn Ferns (*Platycerium* spp.) are popular ornamental plants. They are attached to wayside trees or used as indoor plants. In fact, these ferns have a popular following worldwide and are eagerly sought after by enthusiasts. Other epiphytic ferns that are becoming popular

on wayside trees and indoor displays include the Oak-leaf Fern (*Drynaria* spp.) and Bird's-nest Fern (*Asplenium nidus*). The latter is fast becoming popular as a potted or ground fern.

Ferns are also used in gardens and landscaping. Tree Ferns are becoming popular in landscaping because of their tall trunk and attractive collection of large, highly dissected fronds at the top. The many species and cultivars of the Maidenhair Fern (*Adiantum*) and Ladder Fern (*Nephrolepis*) are a common sight in many gardens and homes.

Above: A pure patch of **Dicranopteris linearis** *growing in an open area at the periphery of the Bukit Timah forest in Singapore. The thicket has been in existence for more than 50 years.*

Right: The large New Guinea **Platycerium wandae** *makes an attractive hanging fern.*

47

The inner tissues of Tree Ferns are also made into attractively shaped vases and pencil holders, while the larger stems are carved into totems for display in the garden. The root masses of Tree Ferns are sometimes fashioned into pots and sold for potting orchids or cut into slabs for growing epiphytic orchids. Planted upside down, their trunks are used in urban gardens to grow epiphytic ferns and orchids. In New Zealand, such trunks are fashioned into decorative items like lamp stands and bases.

*Right: Singapore is currently growing the **Disc Staghorn Fern** (**Platycerium coronarium**) on roadside trees to enhance the attractiveness of the Garden City.*

*Opposite: The **Elkhorn Fern** (**Platycerium bifurcatum** var. **willinckii**) on display in Okinawa, Japan.*

*Below: **Ridley's Staghorn** (**Platycerium ridleyi**) in a private collector's home in Singapore.*

OTHER USES OF FERNS

In New Guinea, the extremely long and tough frond stalks of the Climbing Fern (*Lygodium*) are used as a binding and lashing twine or woven into basketware, known as "Buka baskets". In the Philippines, the leaf stalks of *Lygodium salicifolium* are similarly made into baskets, hats and fancy cases. The Thais split the leaf stalks lengthwise and weave them into elegant ladies' handbags. In western North America, the Indians weave the dark, polished stems of the Maidenhair Fern, *Adiantum pedatum*, into ornamental baskets. The stems of the Climbing Fern (*Stenochlaena palustris*) are used as crude twines or to make inferior baskets. As twines, they are suitable for tying together the bamboo frames of fish traps, as they do not rot easily when submerged in saltwater. Similarly, the pliable stems of resam (*Dicranopteris linearis* and *D. curranii*) are used in Asia in place of ropes.

The durable stems of Tree Ferns (*Cyathea*) have been used as house posts, fences and in bridge construction. For such uses, the trunks are planted upside down. In Hawaii, the scales of Tree Ferns are collected and used for pillow stuffing. The furry golden scales on the base of frond stalks of Tree Ferns and *Sadleria* were once also used for stuffing mattresses in Hawaii. These scales were also used in Hawaii to embalm dead bodies, which could then be kept for up to 8 months before burial. The golden hairs of the Golden Chicken Fern (*Cibotium barometz*) were used to stuff pillows in Britain in the 19th century. For many centuries the Chinese used these golden hairs, as well as the scales of *Cyathea* and *Dicksonia* and the fronds of *Adiantum pedatum* and *Lygodium microphyllum*, to arrest bleeding.

Clubmoss (*Lycopodium*) spores, because of their high oil content, were once used in the production of photographic flash powder, light flashes in theatres, gunpowder and fireworks. They have anti-coagulant properties and have been used to prevent clumping of pills.

Bracken used to be economically important in Britain before 1750. This fern played an important role in the Scottish highlands, being used for thatching and bedding for cattle. Its use as bedding for humans, either in the raw state or as a stuffing for mattresses, goes back at least to Roman times. The ash resulting from burning the plant was used as a source of potash for potato fields, especially in Scotland. This potash was also used for tanning leather and for making soap and glass until alkali became easily available during the 19th century. In northern Britain, the rhizomes of Bracken were sometimes dried in the sun and made into balls of soap for washing clothes.

The stem of the Horsetail Fern (*Equisetum debile, E. arvense, E. hyemale*) contains crystals of silica, making it very useful as a fine sandpaper for polishing wood and smoothing tools. It was used in medieval Europe to scour pots and to polish wood. In New Guinea, it is commonly used to clean cooking and eating utensils. France exports the stems of *Equisetum arvense* for the making of clarinet reeds.

In the highlands of New Guinea, many species of ferns are important components of ceremonial headdresses, while others are used in various body decorations and adornments. These include *Lycopodium* for headdresses, *Polystichum linearis* for hair decoration, and *Pityrogramma calomelanos* for body decoration.

*Opposite: A **Tree Fern** in the grounds of the Bogor Palace in Indonesia.*

*Right: A vase made from the stem of a **Tree Fern**.*

51

Left: Leaf stalks of **Lygodium** *sp. and a Thai lady's handbag made from them.*

Opposite: A **Tree Fern** *root slab used for the growing of* **Ridley's Staghorn (Platycerium ridleyi)**.

Below: **Tree Ferns** *beautifying the grounds of a hotel in the Cameron Highlands, Peninsular Malaysia.*

PROPAGATION OF FERNS

SPORE CULTURE

It is relatively easy to grow fern spores at home. To collect spores, you must first collect mature, fertile fronds. Seek out the fern species you are interested in growing. Look at the undersurface of mature fronds for the presence of sporangia, although some ferns develop their sporangia on specialised outgrowths. Collect only fronds with mature sporangia—at the stage when they are just bursting to disperse their spores. This can be easily recognised by feeling the surface. You can feel the dusty presence of liberated spores among the sporangia. At the immature stage, the sporangia are crisp-looking and the indusia, if present, are neat and smooth. If the indusia are wrinkled and brown and most sporangia have disappeared, it would be futile to collect the frond.

Place the fronds with the mature sporangia between sheets of old newspapers and shine a table lamp on them for a few hours to provide heat to encourage the sporangia to burst. If a lamp is not available, just leave the folded newspaper in a dry place for a few days. If the sporangia on the frond are mature, the

Platycerium bifurcatum with a young "pup" on the left.

spores will be released rapidly. Spores will be released from immature sporangia with difficulty, if at all. Once the spores are liberated, just lift up the frond and tap it lightly. Collect the spores on the paper and store them in a small paper envelope.

Fern spores can also be obtained from the many fern societies found around the world (see listing at the back of this book). Many of these societies maintain spore banks and actively exchange spores with members, so you can easily obtain spores of exotic ferns from far-off lands. The spores come in small paper packets which can be sent through the post. Most fern spores remain viable for months or even years and can thus be conveniently exchanged through the post. However, a handful of species remain viable for a short period and these need to be sown immediately on arrival. As a general rule, the fresher the spores, the better the success rate and speed of germination.

There are a number of ways to grow the spores. You can grow them on clean broken bricks placed in a clean earthenware flowerpot placed in a shallow dish of water. Better still, stand the pot in shallow water contained in a deep plastic tray and cover the tray with a piece of glass or parafilm (plastic film). This is to allow light to get in but keep out weedy fern spores which, in the tropics, can contaminate the spores you are growing. Also, covering the tray will keep mosquitoes from breeding in the water. The spores should be dusted on the surface of the broken bricks. Ensure that the broken bricks are moist at all times. Place the container in a well-lit spot in the garden or verandah but away from direct sun. Instead of broken bricks, a clean, overturned earthenware pot placed in a few centimetres of water in a basin will do just as well.

After about a month or more, assuming that the spores are viable, the surface of the bricks will be covered with green prothalli. Allow the prothalli to develop in the tray until sporelings appear. If the growing surface is too crowded, some of the prothalli can be transplanted onto other pots. Under the moist conditions in the container, fertilisation will occur and in due course sporelings will appear. This is recognised by the appearance of young fronds which stick up from the green mass of prothalli. Once the sporelings have developed two or three fronds, they are large enough to handle and can be transplanted into small pots or trays filled with a well-drained mixture of soil and rubble. Sphagnum moss or coconut fibres can also be used. Place these pots or trays in a shaded place, cover with glass or parafilm, and ensure that there is always sufficient moisture to tide them over the shock of transplanting. Once the sporelings have

developed sufficient roots, they can be slowly hardened by removing the top covering and exposing them to more light. Transplant to bigger pots when necessary.

Top: Fern prothalli growing on the undersurface of an overturned earthernware pot placed in a basin of water.

Centre: Fern prothalli growing on broken brick pieces.

Bottom: Fern sporelings developing from prothalli growing in soil contained in small pots.

1.

1. *Earthenware pot containing broken brick pieces placed in a tray of water under glass cover. Spores are sown on the bricks.*

2. *Earthenware pot placed upside down in a tray of water under glass cover, Spores are sown on the pot surface.*

3. *Sporelings grown in sphagnum moss in a tray of water under glass cover.*

2.

4. *Pot with sporelings removed from tray but with glass covering the top.*

5. *Sporeling in pot with the glass cover removed.*

3.

4.

5.

Spore Culture

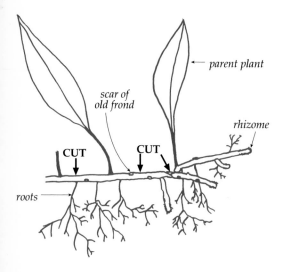

Rhizomes can be cut into pieces and planted separately.

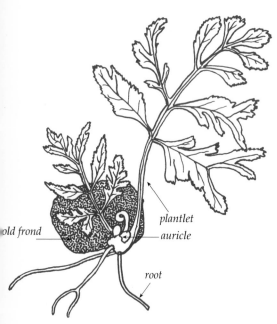

*The swollen base of the old **Elephant Fern** (**Angiopteris evecta**) frond can be detached and planted to induce a plantlet to develop.*

VEGETATIVE PROPAGATION

Ferns with short-creeping rhizomes grow in clumps, forming smaller clumps with the branching of the rhizome. These smaller clumps can easily be separated during repotting. Just shake off the excess soil and carefully separate the different clumps. A spade or secateurs may come in handy in cases where growth is compact. During such divisions, excess roots and old fronds should be trimmed back. Young fronds and new crosiers should be carefully protected. Many Maidenhair Ferns can be divided in this way.

Propagation of ferns with long-creeping rhizomes, either above ground or underground, involves simply cutting off a portion of the rhizome with a few fronds attached and planting it as a separate plant. The presence of roots on the rhizome will ensure survival of the cut piece.

Elephant Fern (*Angiopteris*) and *Marattia* grow in a tight, compact clump. Each of the large fronds has a pair of fleshy ear-like structures, or auricles, surrounding the base of the frond stalk. In old clumps, the remaining pairs of auricles surrounding the base of rotted old fronds develop a plantlet each. These old auricle pairs can be carefully detached from the plant base with a spade and planted separately.

Certain Staghorns produce young, or pups, as they are commonly called. These arise as a result of branching of the short-creeping rhizome, which is normally not seen as it is hidden beneath layers of nest fronds. These pups can be carefully cut off from the parent plant and mounted separately on a Tree Fern slab or piece of wood. The Elkhorn Fern (*Platycerium bifurcatum*) develops pups from root buds, especially when these roots are damaged.

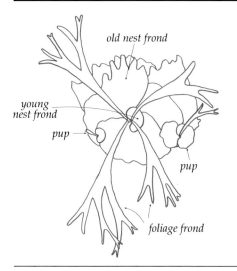

old nest frond

young nest frond

pup

pup

foliage frond

Above: The **Elkhorn Fern** developing young pups.

Below: Four dissected fronds of the **Bird's-nest Fern** (**Asplenium nidus**) *planted to induce the development of plantlets. The frond on the extreme left has a mass of roots still attached, with a plantlet developing from it. The frond second from right has developed a large plantlet and many smaller plantlets, as can be seen by their yellowish young fronds still in the crosier stage.*

The Bird's-nest Fern (*Asplenium nidus*) can be simply cut into two through the growing point to give two separate plants. One half will retain the apical bud and will thus keep on growing to eventually develop its original shape. In the case of the other half without the apical bud, a normally dormant side bud will be triggered and will take over the function of the apical bud. This is a rather drastic method, and unless care is taken not to damage the plant when cutting it into two, the portion without the apical bud may die. This method is usually more successful if the plant is large and well established. It is even possible to cut the plant into four or eight through the growing point to obtain as many separate plants. A method called frond-bud propagation can, theoretically, give as many plantlets as there are fronds on a plant. The method involves isolating an outer frond from the stem and, with the

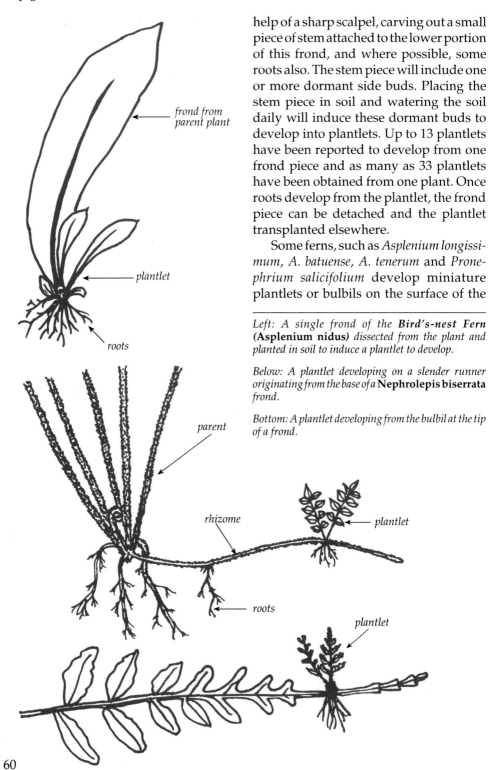

help of a sharp scalpel, carving out a small piece of stem attached to the lower portion of this frond, and where possible, some roots also. The stem piece will include one or more dormant side buds. Placing the stem piece in soil and watering the soil daily will induce these dormant buds to develop into plantlets. Up to 13 plantlets have been reported to develop from one frond piece and as many as 33 plantlets have been obtained from one plant. Once roots develop from the plantlet, the frond piece can be detached and the plantlet transplanted elsewhere.

Some ferns, such as *Asplenium longissimum*, *A. batuense*, *A. tenerum* and *Pronephrium salicifolium* develop miniature plantlets or bulbils on the surface of the

Left: A single frond of the **Bird's-nest Fern** **(Asplenium nidus)** *dissected from the plant and planted in soil to induce a plantlet to develop.*

Below: A plantlet developing on a slender runner originating from the base of a **Nephrolepis biserrata** *frond.*

Bottom: A plantlet developing from the bulbil at the tip of a frond.

frond from parent plant

plantlet

roots

parent

rhizome

plantlet

roots

plantlet

frond, along the midrib, or at the tip of the frond. These are called bulbils because they usually have a bulbous base. As they develop, these plantlets develop roots and can be detached and planted separately.

Nephrolepis produces slender lateral branches or runners from the base of each frond, radiating out in all directions. These runners develop roots along their length and plantlets at intervals. These plantlets in turn develop runners and second generation plantlets and by this method spread rapidly in all directions. In the case of *Nephrolepis cordifolia*, the underground stems develop many rounded tubers. These are storage organs as well as reproductive units. Each can be potted to obtain a separate plant.

Right: Tubers of **Nephrolepis cordifolia***, each developing a plantlet.*

Bottom: Plantlets developing from the tips of **Asplenium tenerum** *fronds.*

Many terrestrial Adder's-tongue Ferns (*Ophioglossum*) produce root buds from their fleshy underground roots. These buds develop into small plants that emerge from the ground and in time become separate plants as the roots connecting them with the parent plant rot away.

The epiphytic Tassel Fern (*Lycopodium phlegmaria*) sometimes produces many plantlets at the ends of the fertile tassels, which develop roots if placed on moist soil. Plantlets can be induced to develop from these branches or even from vegetative cuttings when they are lightly covered with soil and kept moist. Tassel Ferns normally cannot be grown from spores, although there have been cases of laboratory germination of spores.

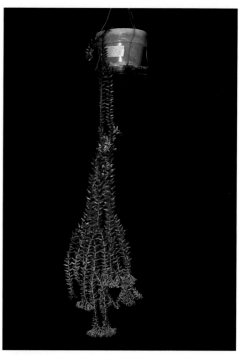

*The **Tassel Fern** (**Lycopodium phlegmaria**) grows on the branches of forest trees. The branches hang down in tassels and develop plantlets from their ends.*

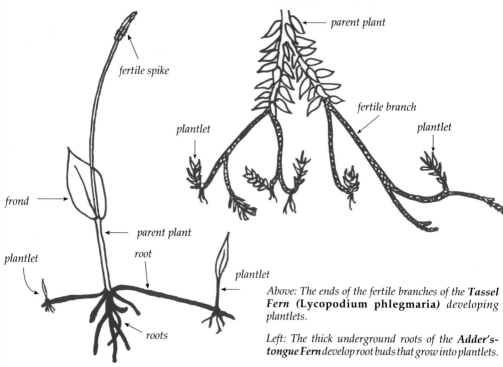

fertile spike

parent plant

plantlet

fertile branch

plantlet

frond

parent plant

root

plantlet

plantlet

roots

*Above: The ends of the fertile branches of the **Tassel Fern** (**Lycopodium phlegmaria**) developing plantlets.*

*Left: The thick underground roots of the **Adder's-tongue Fern** develop root buds that grow into plantlets.*

62

TISSUE CULTURE

Tissue culture has been used as a research tool in the study of plant development since the early 1950s. Its potential as a tool for the rapid multiplication of ferns was only realised in the 1980s. Currently, many countries are mass propagating ferns by this method for the local market as well as for export. Genera propagated by tissue culture for commercial purposes include *Polypodium, Platycerium, Davallia* and *Nephrolepis*.

Tissue culture requires specialised equipment, special nutrient solutions and sterile techniques. However, this does not mean that it can only be undertaken in specialised laboratories. The average fern enthusiast can undertake such a method if care is taken to maintain strict cleanliness and sterile conditions in the technique and equipment. The most important equipment is the autoclave to sterilise the glassware, solutions, forceps and scalpels (or knives). This can be replaced by the pressure cooker, which is easily operated in the kitchen. Glassware like flasks and beakers can be replaced by wide-necked bottles and glass containers, as long as they can withstand the high temperatures of the pressure cooker. Modern tissue culture laboratories use lamina flows which provide a sterile working environment. In the home, an enclosed, draught-free room with a spirit lamp will do.

Basically, the method involves the separation of a small piece of young fern tissue, usually the stem tip or even a young leaf piece, and surface sterilising it in a 5% sodium hypochloride (10% Clorox) solution for about 10 minutes. The piece of tissue is then washed a few times in sterile water before cutting into smaller pieces of around 2 mm square. These smaller pieces,

A tissue-cultured piece of **Platycerium coronarium** *frond developing masses of green calluses.*

or explants as they are called, are then introduced into a flask containing culture medium. The flask opening is sealed with one layer of parafilm followed by a layer of metal foil. It is necessary to flame the scalpel and forceps every time they are used and to flame the flask opening before the cover is removed as well as just before a new cover is put in place.

The culture medium can be separately mixed from inorganic chemicals according to a specific formula. Alternatively, a general premixed medium is available from chemical companies. To the chemical solution is added 1% by volume of agar. The mixture is then heated until the agar is completely dissolved in the solution. The medium is poured into the flask to a depth of about 2 cm, and a piece of metal foil is wrapped round the mouth of the flask. The flasks are then autoclaved for 20 minutes at 122°C. Depending on the fern species, the culture medium may need the addition of hormones such as NAA (a-naphthalene acetic acid), 2,4-D (2-4-dichlorophenoxy acetic acid), and/or kinetin.

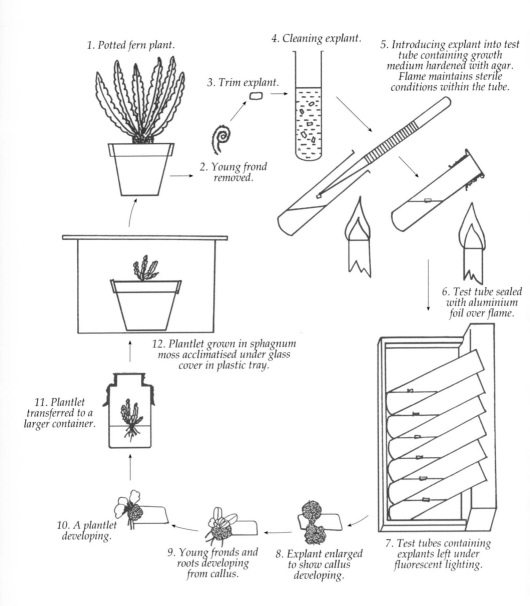

1. Potted fern plant.

2. Young fiond removed.

3. Trim explant.

4. Cleaning explant.

5. Introducing explant into test tube containing growth medium hardened with agar. Flame maintains sterile conditions within the tube.

6. Test tube sealed with aluminium foil over flame.

7. Test tubes containing explants left under fluorescent lighting.

8. Explant enlarged to show callus developing.

9. Young fronds and roots developing from callus.

10. A plantlet developing.

11. Plantlet transferred to a larger container.

12. Plantlet grown in sphagnum moss acclimatised under glass cover in plastic tray.

Tissue Culture

After they have been inoculated with the fern tissues, the flasks should be placed in a reasonably clean room with fluorescent lighting. If there are no signs of bacterial or fungal growth on the medium surface within a few days, it can be assumed that the culture is reasonably free from contamination.

If the operation is successful, calluses (new cells) will form on the explants. The appearance of calluses may take a few weeks or a month or so. The next stage is the production of shoots and roots from the explants. These shoots can be transplanted into new flasks to build up the number of plantlets in culture. When the plantlets are sufficiently large, they can be transplanted out of the flasks into small pots containing potting mixture of sphagnum moss, coconut fibre or vermiculite. During the first week or so, it is advisable to place these pots in a tray containing a few centimetres of water and cover the top with a piece of glass or parafilm. Place the tray indoors with

Platycerium ridleyi *plantlets grown from tissue culture in plastic containers.*

indirect lighting or fluorescent lighting for another few days before transferring it outdoors, under shade. Once the plants have hardened enough, the top covering can be removed, but the pots must be kept moist at all times. Only when the plant is firmly established and new fronds are developing can it be safely transferred to bigger pots for growth in the open.

CULTIVATION OF FERNS

In the tropics, the growing of ferns is relatively simple, as long as certain rules are followed. Ferns need plenty of shade to grow and an abundant supply of moisture. They also need lots of organic matter and good drainage.

In general, ferns prefer shade to open situations. Most of the ferns we encounter are forest ferns and thus they require shade to grow. The epiphytic ferns found growing on trees, even trees along the wayside, are not true sun ferns. They thrive under the shade of the trees on which they grow, and if grown exposed to the full sun they will turn yellow and eventually die. Even those ferns that are found in totally exposed locations, like *Gleichenia* and *Dicranopteris*, can only survive such exposure once they are well established. The early growth of such ferns requires shady and moist conditions.

The degree of shade a fern needs will depend on its original habitat. A forest fern growing under the canopy of trees will need deep shade, while an epiphyte of wayside trees can tolerate open situations, but will still need some shade. A good guide is to observe the fronds, as too much sun will result in the yellowing

and eventual scorching of the fronds. In growing Maidenhair Ferns (*Adiantum* spp.), even under shaded conditions, it may be necessary to monitor the shade at different times of the year, in order to avoid the direct afternoon sun during certain months. Potted Maidenhair Ferns can be moved about as the direct rays of the sun shift during different periods of the year. Excessive exposure results in the young fiddleheads drying. Fleshy ferns like *Angiopteris* need total shade as excessive exposure will result in rapid water loss resulting in the fronds turning flaccid. It is best to experiment with placement of potted ferns to find out the ideal sites for optimum growth.

Ferns need moisture for luxuriant growth, so regular watering is required. However, drainage is essential and thus the composition of the soil is important. Waterlogging is detrimental to growth as the roots are deprived of essential oxygen. Even mangrove ferns like *Acrostichum* have their roots regularly aerated through the daily changes in tidal levels. Epiphytic ferns growing on the branches of trees can tolerate dryness more than other types of ferns. However, with excessive drying even these show signs of yellowing and their fronds become parched. Rain may revive them and trigger new growth.

*A display of **Elkhorn Ferns (Platycerium bifurcatum)**, with a **Bird's-nest Fern** on top of the support.*

SOIL

Ferns can be successfully grown in any soil, as long as there is good drainage and sufficient organic matter for moisture retention and nutrition. Prior to planting on the ground, it is necessary to dig up the soil to a depth of about 20 cm and, depending on the soil type, add soil conditioners, such as commercial compost, garden compost or any other organic matter. If the soil is acidic, lime has to be added. Clay soil tends to be surface compacted, resulting in waterlogging. It is thus necessary to add organic matter, gravel, or sand. On the other hand, sandy soil does not retain water and is nutrient poor, so it is necessary to add loam and a liberal amount of organic matter. In general, well-burnt earth with the addition of compost makes a good potting mixture.

There are a number of polymer-type soil conditioners on the market which, when mixed in the right proportion with soil, will improve the water retention properties of the soil. Their use will decrease the frequency of watering needed and this is especially useful in the cultivation of ferns susceptible to drying, such as Maidenhairs. Even rock ferns grow well in well-drained soil rich in organic matter. Epiphytic ferns grow best on fern-root slabs, pieces of wood or tree branches, or even tied directly on to branches of trees. Organic mulch or sphagnum moss needs to be introduced when these ferns are first mounted onto the medium, both as a source of nutrients and to retain moisture during the early period of establishment.

Adiantum peruvianum *makes a very attractive potted plant for the home.*

FERTILISERS

Ferns favour organic fertilisers to inorganic ones, as the former release nutrients slowly into the soil over an extended period of time. Organic fertilisers include bone meal, dried blood, fish meal, sewerage sludge and treated animal manure. These are best mixed with the soil at the time of planting or repotting. At other times they can be dug into the soil beside the plant.

Inorganic fertilisers can be applied in a liquid form or as solid pellets. They usually come in the form of complete fertilisers containing a range of nutrients. It is necessary to read the labels as certain so-called complete fertilisers contain only nitrogen, phosphorous and potassium. Others may contain all the major and some of the minor nutrients as well. The composition of the major nutrients is also important. High nitrogen favours frond growth, while high phosphorous and potassium favour root growth and spore production. However, it is important to test inorganic fertiliser first on a few plants, as excessive amounts can result in root burns and frond damage. The fertiliser may not be appropriate for the ferns you are growing, so always follow the instructions given on the label. It is always safer to use slow-release inorganic fertilisers, which reduce the danger of damage to roots. Such fertilisers come in granular pellets, large tablets or spikes.

Foliar inorganic fertilisers are also available. These are nutrient mixtures which are dissolved in water and applied as foliar sprays. It is important to follow the recommendations of the manufacturers, as the fronds can easily be damaged if the mixture is too concentrated. The addition of a wetting agent to the mixture will help the solution stick to the frond surface. Foliar sprays can be economical, as the plant can be given just the right amount, without excessive runoff.

PESTS AND DISEASES

Cultivated ferns are constantly under attack from a variety of pests and diseases, especially when the plants are unhealthy or when growing conditions are unfavourable, resulting in the weakening of the plants. Sometimes, regular fertilising of the ferns will ensure their resistance to such attacks. But even healthy ferns can sometimes be attacked by pests and diseases. Generally, they are more susceptible to pests than to diseases. In most cases of pest infestation, manual removal of the causative agents is recommended, rather than use of pesticides.

Sap-sucking insects, including aphids, scale insects, mites and mealy bugs, are usually found on new growths. These insects are usually accompanied by ants, which feed on their sugary secretions. Ants also farm these insects and in the process help spread them to new growths and to other plants. Thus, removing the ants will help contain the insects to a certain extent. A dilute soap solution can be sprayed on the plant to deter insects.

Caterpillars, snails, slugs, weevils, grasshoppers, staghorn weevils and borers are chewing pests that may infest the plant, eating the fronds and leaving the plant unsightly. Slugs and snails destroy new fronds, especially the fiddleheads, thus effectively cutting down new growths. Chewing pests are easily controlled by manual removal during the evening, at night and, in the case of snails and slugs, after rains.

Unless infestation is widespread, chemicals should be avoided as they poison the environment and pollute the atmosphere. It is always unpleasant to spray smelly chemicals, not only for yourself but also for your neighbours. Odourless chemicals do not provide warnings to people nearby, and their presence in the air is a danger to health, especially for babies and young children. Many chemicals are toxic in high concentrations and their effects may be accumulative over long periods of inhalation. So where it is possible to use manual control, avoid chemicals. However, there may be times when it is necessary to resort to chemical control. In such instances you can obtain a variety of pesticides, depending on the type of pests. Use those recommended for ferns, and unless the particular chemical is recommended for the specific species of fern, test it on a few fronds and observe for a few days. This is because many chemical sprays are harmful to ferns, causing frond burns. Read the labels that come with the chemicals and follow the instructions.

There are a number of relatively safe pesticides. Use these instead of those which are more toxic to other life. Rotenone or derris dust is made from the roots of a leguminous creeper, *Derris*. This root has long been used as a natural insecticide and to stun fish in damned streams in many parts of Southeast Asia. It is effective against caterpillars and cutworms and is broken down by sunlight. Pyrethrum is another naturally-occurring compound obtained from the flowers of *Pyrethrum* and *Chrysanthemum*. It effectively controls aphids, caterpillars and bugs when applied as a spray. Sulphur dust can control aphids and mites.

*Opposite: In many gardens the common **Bird's-nest Fern** (**Asplenium nidus**) is encouraged on trees, as shown here in the Singapore Zoological Gardens.*

*Below: The **Lasagne Fern** (**Asplenium nidus** var. **plicatum**) has attractive convoluted and pleated fronds.*

FERN HABITATS

Fern are found in almost every country of the world and in a wide variety of habitats—from lowlands to mountains, from forests to sub-desert scrub, and from coastal mangrove swamps to ponds and rivers. Although these plants exist in almost every habitat, they are not normally dominant in any vegetation. Rather, they depend on other plants to provide a conducive environment for their growth.

Of the 12,000 species of ferns recorded around the world, 65% are believed to be confined to the wet tropics. This richness of fern diversity in the tropics can be attributed to the abundance of rainfall and sunshine, two factors necessary for the proliferation of ferns. The existence of large areas of primary forests, the diversity of vegetation and the presence of mountainous areas are further contributing factors.

This old Rain Tree (Samanea saman) is overgrown with all types of epiphytes—ferns, orchids, dischidias, algae, bryophytes and lichens. The lower trunk is covered with **Pyrrosia longifolia**, *easily recognised by its very long, narrow fronds. Crowding the branches are the shorter fronds of* **P. lanceolata**. **Bird's-nest Ferns (Asplenium nidus)** *grow precariously at various locations on the tree. The mass of leafy growth seen at the point where the branches grow out from the tree trunk is a Strangling Fig (Ficus sp.).*

LOWLAND RAINFOREST

Fern diversity is at its highest in tropical lowland rainforest. Under the forest canopy, humidity is always high and the light level low, and there is little or no air movement. The daily fluctuation in temperature is minimal. Such conditions are ideal for the successful development of the fern prothalli, which generally need weeks to complete the cycle from spore germination to fertilisation. Also, the forest offers a wide range of habitats for ferns, from the forest floor to river banks to the branches of trees.

Ground ferns like *Lindsaea doryphora, Taenitis interrupta* and *Tectaria singaporeana* enjoy the full shade of the forest canopy. Where the canopy is interrupted by tree fall, the light level of the forest floor is increased and sun-loving ferns invade the area. Rivers and streams similarly open up the canopy and the banks are exposed to more sunlight. Larger ferns like *Adiantum, Athyrium, Blechnum, Cyclosorus, Lindsaea, Microlepia, Pronephrium, Pteris* and *Tectaria* are normally well represented in areas where the canopy lets in more light. *Dipteris lobbiana* grows thickly along river banks, as the plant is well adapted to regular flooding after heavy storms. *Lindsaea lucida* and *L. nitida* prefer the rocky banks of forest rivers. Fallen logs

around rivers provide additional habitats for ferns, especially the smaller species such as the Filmy Ferns of the family Hymenophyllaceae.

Rocks, within the forest or by rivers and streams, offer another specialised habitat. The thin layer of decaying organic matter accumulating on the rock surface provides the nutrients necessary for the growth of rock ferns. This relatively unstable growing medium can only support smaller plants like *Antrophyum latifolium*, *Asplenium tenerum*, *Bolbitis appendiculata* and the extremely small

Monogramma trichoidea, which is easily mistaken for a bryophyte.

Conditions are never uniform from forest floor to forest canopy. With increasing height, there is a corresponding increase in air movement, temperature, and light, and a decrease in humidity. At the same time, there is greater fluctuation in all these factors during the daylight hours. High climbers like *Teratophyllum*, *Lomariopsis* and *Lomagramma* start life on the forest floor and climb up tree trunks to reach the forest canopy, where they become fertile. These plants are more tolerant of the higher light and temperature in the upper strata of the forest. Those that are unable to tolerate the less uniform conditions remain around the base of trees, as is the case for low climbers like *Lindsaea repens* and *L. parasitica*.

Epiphytes are an interesting group that have exploited a specialised habitat on the

Opposite (top): A view of the tropical rainforest at Muka Head, Pulau Pinang.

Opposite (bottom): Profile of a tropical rainforest as seen from a logging road at Endau-Rompin, Peninsular Malaysia.

Below: A stream running through the rainforest at Cameron Highlands, Peninsular Malaysia.

trunks and branches of trees. These epiphytes do not in any way harm the host tree. They merely borrow the support provided by the tree. As their roots do not touch the ground, they need special abilities to obtain water and nutrients high on the branches of the trees. *Davallia triphylla* and *Humata angustata* creep along the branches, their roots tapping the decaying organic matter accumulating between the flaky bark. The leaves of *Asplenium nidus* form open baskets to collect falling leaves and other organic litter. These composting leaves held within the nest provide nutrients and absorb moisture for the fern to use. Staghorn Ferns (*Platycerium coronarium, P. wallichii, P. platylobium*) have developed the most efficient litter-trapping device. Their nests can develop into extremely large and heavy masses that may one day topple off the branch of the host tree.

MOUNTAIN FOREST

The lowland rainforest is dominated by the large timber trees of the botanical family Dipterocarpaceae. With increasing altitude, the forest changes in character. The canopy becomes lower, there are fewer tall trees jutting out of the canopy, epiphytic ferns and orchids become abundant, and there is an increase in the presence of mosses and liverworts growing on tree trunks, the forest floor, rock surfaces and fallen logs.

Tree Ferns (*Cyathea, Cibotium*) are common features of mountain forest. They often grow beside streams and can reach 10 metres or greater in height, the largest being *C. contaminans*. They are a familiar sight in the mountain resorts of Cameron Highlands, Fraser's Hill, Maxwell Hill and Genting Highlands in Malaysia. The Tree Fern's single tall trunk, with its bunch of

large, much dissected fronds at the top, can hardly be missed. The Golden Chicken Fern (*Cibotium barometz*) is one of the less spectacular Tree Ferns as far as height is concerned. However, the growing point, with its thick covering of golden hairs, is eagerly collected for sale.

Mountain rainforest above the elevation of 1,200 metres usually supports a richer epiphytic fern flora. The epiphytic ant fern, *Lecanopteris carnosa*, is common. Its hollow, swollen rhizomes form a crust around the branches of tall trees. Other common epiphytes include *Aglaomorpha*, *Antrophyum*, *Belvesia*, *Crypsinus*, *Drynaria rigidula*, *Elaphoglossum*, *Humata* and *Merinthosorus*.

At around 1,500 metres and above, the trees become shorter and denser. There is an abundance of epiphytic bryophytes swathing the boles and crowns of trees. This is the so-called mossy forest of the upper mountain forest. It is extremely rich in ferns, especially epiphytic ferns of the families Hymenophyllaceae and Grammitidaceae. The former includes *Hymenophyllum*, *Trichomanes* and related genera; the latter *Arcosorus*, *Calymmodon*, *Ctenopteris*, *Grammitis*, *Scleroglossum* and *Xiphopteris*. Various species of *Lycopodium* are common and can be seen growing from the ground between the dwarfed trees, and even from the branches of these trees. The increase in epiphytic ferns and bryophytes is associated with the decrease in temperature and increase in humidity at high altitude. Overhanging clouds contribute to these conditions and reduce the sun's burning rays. At night, heavy clouds totally cover the trees. The fern

Opposite: Sungei Sedili Kechil, Johor.

*Below: A grove of **Tree Ferns** in a cleared forest patch at Fraser's Hill resort in Peninsular Malaysia.*

diversity of mountain forest make it the richest of all habitats.

SECONDARY FOREST

When tropical rainforests, especially lowland forests, are exploited for their timber, the larger timber trees are felled and dragged out through crude roads bulldozed through the forest. The opening of the canopy as a result of these activities has an adverse effect on the micro-climate of the forest. Temperature increases, humidity decreases, and more sunlight reaches the forest floor. The forest composition changes as the more aggressive and light-demanding plants invade these open areas. Shade plants, including shade ferns, are phased out as climatic conditions become unsuitable for their survival. Light demanding ferns such as *Blechnum orientale*, *Nephrolepis biserrata*, *Lygodium* spp., and *Lycopodium cernuum* begin to appear. In exploited secondary forests where the soil is nutrient poor, bare areas become colonised by *Dicranopteris*, *Gleichenia* and *Pteridium*, which form thickets to the total exclusion of other plants. These ferns may maintain pure stands for years or even decades.

Opposite: Dwarfed trees in the upper mountain forest at Gunong Ulu Kali in the Genting Highlands.

Below: Upper mountain forest at Gunong Ulu Kali in the Genting Highlands. Note the absence of the tall trees seen in the lowland forest. Trees here are dwarfed and rich in epiphytes.

AGRICULTURAL AREAS

Where forests are replaced by plantation agriculture, shade ferns totally disappear, and in their place weedy sun ferns are quick to appear. Rubber plantations are not especially rich in ferns. The rubber trees themselves do not provide conducive habitats for epiphytic ferns, except for the Disc Staghorn (*Platycerium coronarium*) and a number of climbing epiphytes like *Pyrrosia piloselloides* and *P. longifolia*. Besides, good agricultural practice demands the removal of epiphytes on the trees. In young rubber areas the ground around the trees is kept free of plant growth by regular chemical or manual weeding, and the spaces between trees are covered with a dense growth of legumes. However, as the rubber matures and the canopy becomes more or less complete, very few plants grow under the trees except the Grass Fern (*Schizaea digitata*). Sometimes a thick stand of the smallish *Pronephrium triphyllum* may be found.

Oil palm plantations, on the other hand, are extremely rich in ferns, particularly sun-loving epiphytic species. As the old palm leaves fall off, their bases persist on the stem for months, if not years. These leaf bases collect dust and rotting organic matter and are excellent growing points for a number of epiphytic ferns. On old palms, there is always a collection of ferns covering the entire length of the stem. Such ferns include *Goniophlebium percus-*

*Opposite (top): The mossy forest at Gunong Ulu Kali in the Genting Highlands, with the tree trunk covered with a thick growth of bryophytes and **Filmy Ferns** of the family Hymenophyllaceae.*

Opposite (bottom): A logged forest in Beluntu, Johor.

Below: A rubber plantation fronting Gunong Panti, Johor.

sum, Asplenium nidus, Pyrrosia piloselloides, P. longifolia, Nephrolepis acutifolia, Phymatosorus scolopendria and *Vittaria ensiformis*. On the ground below, especially at the edge of the plantation where there is more light, weedy ferns like *Nephrolepis biserrata* may form dense stands.

SWAMPS AND OPEN WATERS

A watery environment is not the best habitat for ferns, and only a few species are adapted to survive under such conditions. True water ferns like *Salvinia* and *Azolla* prefer to grow on the surface of polluted ponds and lakes. However, in rice fields, where the water level varies with the planting cycle, these ferns, together with *Marsilea crenata* and *Ceratopteris thalictroides*, may take root in the soft mud when the water is drained towards the harvesting period. They are

subsequently ploughed into the soil to contribute to its organic content.

In freshwater swamps, the most common fern is *Stenochlaena palustris*, which thrives in soggy grounds. The plant is a climber, and it sometimes forms thickets in wet ground.

Mangrove swamps, which occur by river mouths and along coastal areas, are inundated by the rising tide twice a day. The soil here is silt-rich and saline, and only a handful of highly specialised trees are able to survive under such conditions. Typical mangrove trees like *Avicennia*, *Rhizophora* and *Brugueria*, with their stilt roots, breathing roots, water storage

Opposite: An old oil palm plantation in Johor.

Below: An urban patch of swampy land overgrown with weeds in Singapore. The waterlogged area in the centre of the picture is covered with a thicket of **Stenochlaena palustris**.

tissues, and ability to excrete salt from their leaves, are well adapted to the soft mud and saline conditions. Only one genus of fern, *Acrostichum*, can survive in such conditions. It grows on earth banks and on mud lobsters mounds. In areas where the mangrove trees are cleared, this fern may develop into thick stands.

URBAN AREAS

Unlike rainforests, built-up areas have very high temperatures and low humidity because of the scarcity of trees and the presence of concrete buildings and tarred roads. Temperatures can be extremely high during the day, falling towards evening when humidity increases. Despite the high rainfall in the tropics, moisture retention is low due to the extensive drainage systems, although during periods of heavy rainfall, certain areas may be flooded. Roadside

trees are planted in many urban areas to reduce the high temperatures of the day, but these so-called urban forests are nowhere near as effective as the rainforests at modifying the climatic conditions. The only ferns that can survive in urban areas are sun ferns, and roadside trees provide excellent habitats for their growth. Older roadside trees such as the Angsana (*Pterocarpus indicus*), Sea Apple (*Eugenia grandis*), Broad-leafed Mahogany (*Swietenia macrophylla*), Mexican Lilac (*Glircidia sepium*), Sea Almond (*Terminalia catappa*) and Rain Tree (*Samanea saman*) invariably harbour epiphytic ferns. Of these, the South American Rain Tree, commonly planted along roads in many Southeast Asian countries, is the tree most heavily laden with ferns and epiphytic orchids.

There are many reasons why this tree is overgrown with epiphytes. The wide-spreading branches provide convenient

places for ferns to establish, while the scaly bark helps trap dust and moisture, which helps germinating spores to survive the early stages of their development. The folding of the leaves at around 5 o'clock every evening, as well as before a storm, allows for dew and rain to effectively reach the inner areas of the crown—the surface of the branches and main trunk where such ferns are found.

Young roadside trees very seldom harbour epiphytic growth, as the sexual stage of the fern's cycle would not be able to survive the extremely harsh conditions the trees are exposed to. During the day the sun shines directly onto the tree, so the temperature on the surface of the branches and trunk is high. Humidity is thus low and moisture is available only during rains and after sunset, when the temperature drops and dew forms. Even then, the moisture is not retained for long. It takes years for these harsh conditions to be sufficiently modified for ferns to appear.

Young trees trap dust blown off the road between the cracks of their bark. This accumulation of dirt allows moisture to be retained for a slightly longer period. Algae are the first obvious microorganisms to be attracted to these small pockets of dirt. As the algae die, their dead cells add to the reservoir of organic matter. With time, sufficient organic matter is accumulated to support the establishment of slightly larger organisms, mainly mosses and liverworts. As these bryophytes grow and die, their dead tissues in turn contribute to the accumulating organic matter. Gradually, the water retention properties of such pockets of dirt improves. It is only then that fern spores are able to germinate and survive the early sexual phase. The more common ferns are the Dragon's-scale Fern (*Pyrrosia piloselloides*), Bird's-nest Fern (*Asplenium nidus*), Oak-leaf Fern (*Drynaria*) and the larger Disc Staghorn (*Platycerium coronarium*).

Urban areas also provide habitats for ferns in private gardens and on disused land, drains, hedges, old buildings, and even on newer blocks of apartments. Sun ferns like *Lygodium microphyllum* and *L. flexuosum* are common along hedges and in open areas, scrambling over shrubs and trees. Old buildings and other built-up structures are favourite habitats for a small number of ferns, the commonest being *Pteris vittata*, *Nephrolepis biserrata* and sometimes even *Pyrrosia piloselloides* and *Asplenium nidus*. The tropical American Silver Fern (*Pityrogramma calomelanos*), which was brought into the tropics as an ornamental plant, is now a common weed of open grounds and gardens.

Opposite: A mangrove forest in Benut, Johor.

Below: Old buildings may be overgrown with a variety of ferns and Strangling Figs.

FERN SPECIES

1 – *Acrostichum aureum*

The **Swamp Fern** grows on earth banks and mud lobster mounds in mangrove swamps, usually towards the landward side where the water is brackish. The fronds are tall, growing up to 4 metres high, with oblique, upward-pointing pinnae. Young fronds are pink, while the upper pinnae of old fronds are sometimes black, due to the presence of a thick layer of sporangia. Where the mangrove trees are cleared, this fern can become weedy, developing rapidly on the cleared ground.

Cultivation: Although in nature it proliferates under brackish conditions, plants survive in pots or the ground even when given salt-free water. It can grow under the full sun as long as it is kept well watered.

1a▲   1b▼   1c▶

*1a – Dense patches of **Acrostichum aureum** in a degraded mangrove area by the coast. Note the darker fertile pinnae at the upper end of some fronds.*

*1b – A young **Acrostichum aureum** plant with simple fronds growing between the buttress roots of a mangrove tree. The newly emerging frond in the centre of the plant is still reddish.*

*1c – Towards the seaward side of the mangrove, where the water has a higher salt content, grows the more tolerant species, **Acrostichum speciosum**. Note the fertile fronds with their upper pinnae black with sporangia.*

2▲   3a▼

2 – *Adiantum caudatum*

This slender **Maidenhair Fern** of the lowland rainforest is common on limestone hills in Peninsular Malaysia. The plant has a short, erect rhizome that bears a tuft of simple pinnate fronds. As with most Maidenhairs, the stalks are black and shiny.

Cultivation: Plantlets are readily available from frond tips. These can be planted in a hanging pot or basket or even among rocks. The soil should be well-drained and rich in organic matter, with regular additions of lime.

3 – *Adiantum latifolium*

This is an American fern, indigenous to the region around Central America and the northern areas of South America. It was introduced into Peninsular Malay-sia more than 20 years ago and has so far become naturalised, growing profusely among the undergrowth of rubber plantations. In Singapore, it is invading the primary rainforest at Bukit Timah, growing at the forest edge where there is slightly more light. It has also been found elsewhere, growing among secondary vegetation.

Cultivation: This is a hardy fern requiring light shade, loamy to clayey soil, and warm to cool conditions.

---

2 – **Adiantum caudatum**.

3a – A patch of **Adiantum latifolium** *growing among the leaf litter in a nature park in Pasir Panjang, Singapore.*

3b – The edge of the Bukit Timah forest in Singapore with patches of **Adiantum latifolium** *at left and right.*

3b▼

91

4 – *Aglaomorpha heraclea*

This epiphyte of the mountain forest is a litter-collecting fern with only one type of frond. The frond is large and simple but deeply lobed. The frond base is broad and rounded, and this helps it to accumulate litter. The fronds persist on the plant when dead. The blades are gradually discarded, leaving only the bare midrib behind.

Cultivation: This is a cool climate fern but has been known to survive cultivation in the tropical lowlands. Pieces of stem can be attached to various media suitable for epiphytic ferns and orchids. If successfully rooted to the medium, the fern can be left under shade and kept moist. It can also be planted in a container using a coarse planting mixture allowing for good drainage. Under cool conditions it can be left in partial shade and regularly watered.

5 – *Angiopteris evecta*

This **Elephant Fern** is a lowland forest plant. It has a massive mound of a stem, the outer part of which is covered with the persistent, large and swollen bases of old fronds. Fronds are very large and twice pinnate compound and are borne on thick, fleshy stalks. The extensions of the stalks bear side stalks from which arise the pinnules. The base of the main stalk and side stalks are swollen and the cells filled with water. Turgor pressure keeps the entire frond erect, as there are no hard tissues. During dry periods, water is lost from these cells, resulting in the drooping of the pinnae and the collapse of the entire frond.

Cultivation: Plantlets developing from swollen frond bases can be removed and planted separately in loamy soil rich in humus. These plants can tolerate warm to cool conditions but should not

4▼

be exposed to the direct rays of the sun. They cannot tolerate drying conditions.

---

4 – **Aglaomorpha heraclea**.

5a – The base of **Angiopteris evecta** *showing the stem covered with the swollen bases of old fronds. The bases of three frond stipes are visible. Those on the left and the right have a pair of thick, black structures called auricles subtending the base.*

5b – A fertile **Angiopteris evecta** *pinnule with the sori along the margin. Each sorus is made up of two short rows of sporangia at the end of a vein.*

5c – A large **Angiopteris evecta** *made up entirely of huge, compound fronds, each borne on a long stalk. The brownish mound from which the frond stalks arise is the stem.*

5a▲   5b▼

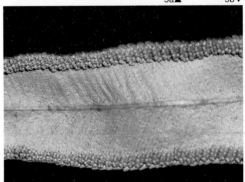

5c▼

93

6a▲   6b▼

6 – *Asplenium longissimum*

This ground fern of slightly open locations proliferates along forest paths and wooded areas where there is sufficient shade and moisture. It is sometimes found growing as an epiphyte from the persistent leaf bases of old oil palms. The pinnate compound frond keeps elongating until a bud develops at the tip. It can often reach 1 metre or longer. The bud takes root when the frond touches the ground some distance from the parent plant.

Cultivation: Sporelings with roots can be removed from old leaf tips and grown in well-drained soil exposed to indirect light.

7 – *Asplenium macrophyllum*

This fern prefers sheltered locations and grows on rocks or trees in lowland rainforest and areas by the sea. It is very common on the Peninsular Malaysian island of Pulau Tioman.

Cultivation: The plant needs a well-drained, humus-rich soil and plenty of shade.

6a – A patch of **Asplenium longissimum** *growing along a forest path. The long, pinnate compound fronds arch out from the central growing point to touch the ground some distance away. Where the terminal pinnae have fully expanded, the frond has completed its growth.*

6b – The undersurface of **Asplenium longissimum** *pinnae showing the elongated sori on both sides of the midrib. The narrow indusium protecting each sorus is attached along a vein, opening towards the midrib. Masses of sporangia can be seen.*

7 – **Asplenium macrophyllum**.

7▼

8a▲   8b▼

8 – *Asplenium nidus*

Bird's-nest Ferns, which grow in lowland, mountain and secondary forests, on wayside trees and in urban areas, are very efficient litter collectors. The whorls of fronds arising from a common central growing point form a nest-like basket. Leaves falling from the support tree accumulate in the "nest". As new fronds grow from the centre of the nest, the accumulated leaves are held firmly between the frond bases. Roots grow through the decaying organic mass to further hold it firmly in place. The entire mass forms a sort of sponge, soaking up rain water for the plant's subsequent use. These ferns are very common on roadside trees.

Cultivation: Young plants can be collected from around old nests and attached to the branch of a tree or planted in the ground or in pots filled with any type of well-drained soil. Bird's-nest Ferns can tolerate the full sun, although this may result in yellowing of the fronds. They can survive dry conditions and tolerate reasonably cool conditions.

---

*8a – Very old **Bird's-nest Ferns** on an old Rain Tree. The fronds, brown with age and hanging down limply, will slowly disintegrate.*

*8b – A row of **Bird's-nest Ferns** growing on a horizontal branch of a Rain Tree.*

8c – A large fern with the whorls of fertile fronds viewed from below. The brown sporangia are arranged in parallel rows, running slightly oblique to the black midrib of the frond. The old fronds collect below the nest, showing varying degrees of disintegration. Sometimes, when the nest becomes very large and heavy, the plant may become dislodged from the tree.

8c▼

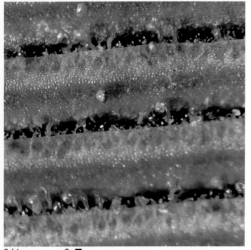

8d▲ 8e▼

8f▼ 8g►

*8d – Indusia of the **Bird's-nest Fern**. The blackish, oval heads emerging from the free ends of the indusia are mature sporangia packed with spores. The light-brown oval structures are the sporangial shells, each with an annulus still attached to it. The annuli are darker brown, curly structures with cross bands. The light-brown dust around the sporangial shells and all over the surface of the frond are the discharged spores.*

*8e – **Bird's-nest Ferns** sometimes establish on buildings. This one is growing at the edge of the roof of a block of terrace houses.*

*8f – A very young **Bird's-nest Fern** growing between the flaky bark of a Rain Tree trunk. Even at this young age, it is starting to collect falling leaves between its nest fronds. The flaky bark of the tree collects dust blown off the road, providing a medium for the growth of microscopic blue-green algae. The mucilage coat of the algae helps to accumulated dirt and also retains moisture, which in turn provides a suitable environment for the germination and further growth of the fern.*

*8g – **Bird's-nest Ferns** have a rather wide distribution, from lowlands to the mountain forests. They are seen here growing on young trees in the Cameron Highlands, Peninsular Malaysia.*

9 – *Asplenium tenerum*

Closely related to the Bird's-nest Fern, *Asplenium tenerum* forms a rather small nest with its pinnate compound fronds to trap falling leaves. It is an epiphyte of moist, shady forest and grows on the lower trunk of small trees or on the side of rocks. Often, the tip of the fronds bears a bud which grows into a young plant, complete with roots.

Cultivation: The entire plant can be carefully removed from the tree trunk or rock surface, attached to fern root slabs, and placed in a shady, warm location. It should be watered regularly. Sphagnum moss or coconut fibres can be inserted between the plant and the growing medium to allow for better water retention during the initial stage of transplanting. It can also be potted, using a coarse, well-drained mixture.

9a▲   9b▼

9a – **Asplenium tenerum** *growing from the side of a large, bryophyte-covered boulder in the Bukit Timah Nature Reserve in Singapore. Although the trap is not anyway near as efficient as that of the Bird's-nest Fern, it would appear to serve its purpose, as seen by the litter trapped between the fronds in this picture.*

9b – **Asplenium tenerum** *growing on the trunk of a forest tree in Pulau Tioman, off the east coast of Peninsular Malaysia.*

10 – *Azolla pinnata*

The small, free-floating **Mosquito Fern** is so called because its thick growth on the water surface is supposed to prevent mosquitoes from breeding. It grows on freshwater ponds, stagnant streams and rice fields. Its overlapping fronds consist of two lobes. The lower, submerged lobe harbours a blue-green alga, *Anabaena azollae*, which is capable of fixing atmospheric nitrogen. Because of this, the fern is especially encouraged in rice fields as its presence enriches the nitrogen content of the soil.

Cultivation: Plants can be cultured in standing water under the full sun. They tolerate cold to warm conditions.

10a▲   10b▼

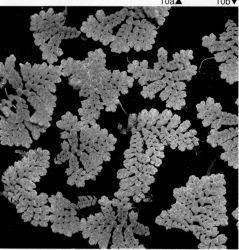

*10a – The **Mosquito Fern** growing on the surface of a fresh water pond among the large floating leaves of the Water Lily. The fern is normally green but here it appears red, a result of aging or overexposure to the sun.*

*10b – Floating **Mosquito Ferns** showing the characteristic branching and fronds in alternating rows. The long, unbranched roots can be seen trailing below the plants.*

10c – A close-up of the upper lobe of the frond, showing the many small projections on the surface.

10c▼

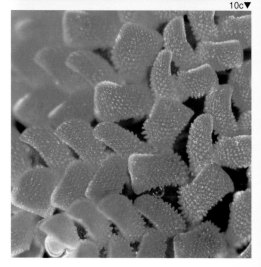

11▲   12a▼

102

12b▲

11 – *Belvisia revoluta*

This is a fairly common epiphyte of forest trees at altitudes above 1,000 metres. The sterile fronds are simple and elongated. The fertile fronds have an extended narrow fertile portion.
Cultivation: Plants can be induced to root on damp sphagnum moss under cool, moist and shaded conditions.

12 – *Blechnum orientale*

This is a very common ground fern of open places in the lowlands. The large, pinnate compound fronds are borne on long stalks. At the base of the stalks are short, leafy projections. The pinnae are narrow and elongated, with the sori in bands on both sides of the midrib.

Cultivation: Young plants can be transplanted into pots or grown in the ground under light shade with plenty of water. Once established, the plant can be exposed to the full sun as long as it is well watered. Soil should be well-drained loam mixed with garden compost. Plants are sensitive to the cold.

---

11 – **Belvisia revoluta**.

12a – **Blechnum** *growing along both banks of a forest stream in the catchment forest in Singapore.*

12b – The young frond of **Blechnum** *is pink. The stipe bears small leafy projections, hence the Malay name of* paku lipan, *or Centipede Fern.*

13 – *Bolbitis appendiculata*

Previously known as *Egenolfia append-iculata*, this rock fern is usually found around streams in the lowland rain-forest. Typical of many forest ferns, the sterile fronds are distinctly different from the fertile fronds. Fronds are pinnate compound, with the fertile pinnae very much shorter and narrower than the sterile. The fertile fronds are much longer and are held high rather than arching outwards. Often, the tips of the sterile fronds develop buds, which grow into plantlets and take root some distance away from the parent.

Cultivation: Plants can be removed easily from the rock surface or sporelings collected from old frond tips. These can be grown in well-drained soil rich in humus, placed in a warm and shaded location and watered regularly.

◄13   14▼

14 – *Bolbitis heteroclita*

Commonly found on stream banks in the lowland rainforest, this fern is also found growing on rocks, earth banks, and the lower trunk of forest trees. The fronds are simple or pinnate compound, in which case the pinnae are large and few in number. The terminal pinna is usually extended at the apex into an elongated structure, with a plantlet developing from the tip.

Cultivation: Plants are easily grown in humus-rich soil given shade and plenty of water.

---

13 – An erect fertile frond of **Bolbitis appendiculata** *growing among the arching sterile fronds. Note the pairs of opposite fertile pinnae with the lower surface of the narrow blade covered yellow with sporangia.*

14 – **Bolbitis heteroclita**.

15 – *Cheilanthes tenuifolia*

A common lowland fern of open places, the **Lip Fern** grows among grasses on earth banks as well as on rocks and old walls. The much dissected fronds are thrice pinnate compound and show dimorphism. Fertile fronds are larger, on longer stalks and stand erect above the sterile.

Cultivation: Plants can be grown in well-drained soil with light shade and warm conditions.

16 – *Cheiropleuria bicuspis*

This unusual fern with a bilobed frond is found growing on shaded rocks in lowland and mountain forests. Fertile fronds are simple and covered with sporangia on the undersurface. They stand erect on long stalks.

15▲   16▼

17 – *Cibotium barometz*

Commonly called **Golden Chicken Fern** because of the thick, golden hairs on the rhizome and the base of the frond stalks, *Cibotium* consists of about a dozen species found in mountain forests in Southeast Asia, Hawaii and Central America. Many are Tree Ferns, although this species is usually without a prominent stem. The golden hairs were once used to arrest bleeding wounds. Today, people collect the apical portions and sell them to gullible tourists and urban dwellers as a charm to ward off evil. It is common in mountain forest, becoming prolific in areas where the forest is disturbed.

Cultivation: Young plants can be transplanted and grown in a humus-rich, well-drained soil. They require plenty of water. The plant can be grown under warm to cool conditions.

17a▲ 17b▼

17c▼

15 – **Cheilanthes tenuifolia** *growing on a regularly mown grassy slope among the common grasses and their associated weeds.*

16 – **Cheiropleuria bicuspis**.

17a – A large **Cibotium barometz** *growing at the Penang Botanic Gardens. This 1984 picture shows, second from left, the late Prof. R. E. Holttum, a world-renowned expert on fern classification.*

17b – The growing point of **Cibotium barometz** *showing the base of the frond stalks densely covered with golden hairs.*

17c – The frond of **Cibotium barometz** *can be as long as 3 metres, including the 1.2-metre brown-black stalk which is smooth except for the thick golden hairs at the base. The frond is twice pinnate compound, with the pinnules deeply lobed.*

18 – *Colysis pedunculata*

This fern is sometimes epiphytic, growing on the lower trunk of trees near streams in lowland and mountain forests. It has also been found growing on boulders in the forest or even on the ground. Fronds are simple and short-stalked. However, fertile fronds are long-stalked, standing erect above the sterile fronds. The sporangia are packed on the lower surface of the smaller lamina area and appear yellow when immature.

Cultivation: Pieces of rhizome can be wrapped in sphagnum moss or coconut fibres and kept well watered in a shady place to get the roots to establish. Plants can be attached to fern root slabs and kept away from the direct sun in warm locations and exposed to indirect sun under cooler conditions.

19 – *Crypsinus wrayi*

A common epiphyte of mountain forests, this smallish fern is usually found at altitudes of 1,300–1,700 metres. Fronds are simple, the sterile shorter and wider than the fertile. Fertile fronds bear a single row of round sori on each side of the midrib.

Cultivation: Plants can be grown on sphagnum moss attached to various media suitable for epiphytes and grown under cool, moist and shaded conditions.

◄18   19a▲   19b▼

---

18 – **Colysis pedunculata**.

19a – **Crypsinus wrayi** *growing on the bryophyte-covered branch of a small tree. The sterile fronds are oval and shorter than the narrower, longer fertile fronds.*

19b – A very narrow fertile frond with sori developing beyond the edge of the frond.

20 – *Ctenopteris obliquata*

This rather small epiphytic fern is common on mossy trees at altitudes of 1,200–2,000 metres. Fronds are pinnate compound, with the sporangia sunk in oblique cavities on the pinnae.

Cultivation: Plants can be attached to various media suitable for epiphytes and grown under cool, moist and shaded conditions.

21 – *Cyathea contaminans*

Tree Ferns are easily recognised by their large fronds grouped at the top of the tall trunk, looking very much like palms. There are about 700 species, of which *Cyathea contaminans* is the tallest. This is a mountain species, found at altitudes of up to 1,700 metres, although it is also seen in fairly low altitudes, especially near rivers. The species is easily recognised by the presence of many thorns at the base of the frond stalk, which has a bluish-green colour.

Cultivation: This fern grows well in cool climates, where it can tolerate the full sun. It can be grown in the lowlands of the tropics, but shade and plenty of water need to be provided, and even then the plant will not be its vigorous self. The soil should contain plenty of organic matter. There are reports that the top portion of the stem can be cut off and transplanted without roots.

---

20 – **Ctenopteris obliquata**.

21a – A tall specimen of **Cyathea contaminans** *amidst the rainforest in Malaysia. The town of Taiping is in the background.*

◀ 20   21a▼

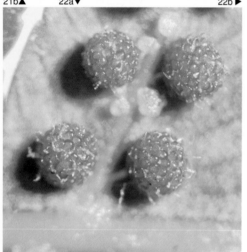

21b▲   22a▼   22b ▶

23▼

22 – *Cyathea latebrosa*

This is very common **Tree Fern** found in the lowlands as well as to an altitude of 1,000 metres or more. The stem is slender and never as tall as the mountain *C. contaminans*. It is also found in secondary forest and among the undergrowth in rubber and oil palm plantations.
Cultivation: This Tree Fern needs plenty of water and organic matter, as well as warm to cool conditions to survive. It should not be exposed to the full sun.

23 – *Cyathea moluccana*

This is another lowland forest **Tree Fern,** found in mountains to an altitude of 1,000 metres. It is different from most other Tree Ferns of the genus *Cyathea* in that its fronds are pinnate compound, instead of twice pinnate.
Cultivation: Plants can be grown in well-drained soil with plenty of organic matter. They need shade and plenty of water, and preferably cool conditions.

21b – A **Tree Fern** *crown with the mass of large, twice pinnate compound fronds radiating from the top of the trunk.*

22a – Four global sori on the underside of a **Cyathea latebrosa** *pinnule. The sporangia are packed tightly together.*

22b – A medium-sized **Cyathea latebrosa** *growing in the secondary forest at Seletar, Singapore. The brown structures leaning against the stem are old fronds. The pinnae have dropped off to leave only the stalks and their extensions.*

23 – The undersurface of a fertile frond of **Cyathea moluccana**. *Each pinna has a number of irregular rows of sori on either side of the midrib.*

24 – *Davallia denticulata*

The **Rabbit's-foot Fern** is so called because of the presence of dense brown scales on the rhizome, causing the rhizome to resemble a rabbit's foot. It is a large fern with finely dissected fronds that are used in flower decorations. Its spores may start life in the nest of the Bird's-nest Fern or the Staghorn Fern, eventually creeping out and growing independently of the nest. The fern grows in secondary forest, oil palm plantations and urban areas.

Cultivation: Pieces of rhizome can be easily grown in soil or attached to branches of trees with the help of coconut fibres and kept damp all the time. Established plants can tolerate the direct sun and drying conditions. This is a hardy fern. It can be grown in warm to cool areas, although it is sensitive to frost.

---

*24a – Close-up of the final segments of the fertile frond of the **Rabbit's-foot Fern**, showing the sori enclosed within cup-shaped indusia. A vein ends at the base of each sorus. Together, they look like a miniature stalked tulip.*

*24b – **Rabbit's-foot Ferns** are commonly seen on the trunks of old oil palms, growing from the rich, organic matter collected between the persistent leaf bases and the trunk.*

24a▼   24b▶

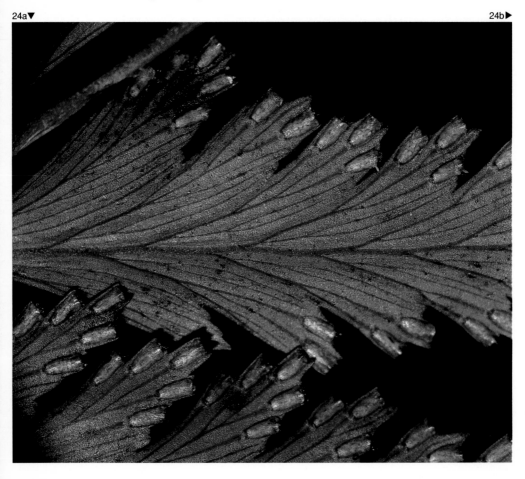

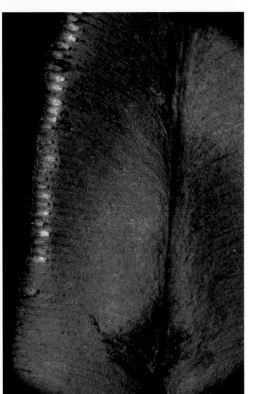

25 – *Davallia triphylla*

This epiphyte of the lowland rainforest is seldom seen, as it grows on tall trees. Once in a while when the branches from these trees break, the fern may land on the forest floor and continue to grow on boulders. Like the Rabbit's-foot Fern of roadside trees, *Davallia triphylla* is a creeper, but the fronds are trifoliate, that is, there are three pinnae at the end of the stipe.

Cultivation: It should be reasonably simple to grow the fern from rhizome pieces, initially wrapping the pieces in sphagnum moss or coconut fibres and keeping them damp all the time until the roots become established. The plants should be kept in a warm, shaded place.

25a▲   25b▼

26 – *Dicranopteris*

Dicranopteris linearis and *D. curranii* are thicket-forming ferns of open places. They are commonly seen in urban areas, growing where the soil is poor and the area fully exposed to the sun. They also form thickets in lowland forests, in areas where the trees are cleared, and in mountain forests. The fronds keep on growing for a long time. After each period of elongation, the tip stops growing and a pair of side branches develop. These side branches in turn elongate to develop further pairs of side branches. Ultimately, the frond is a large, clumsy structure unable to stand erect, collapsing to get entangled with the other fronds. This results in a dense thicket where no other plants are able to grow. The thicket thus maintains its purity for a long time.

Cultivation: Pieces of rhizomes with roots can be planted in clayey soil and exposed to the full sun. The plant prefers warm conditions but can survive cooler locations.

25a – A pinna of **Davallia triphylla** *showing the indusia at the tips of veins arranged side-to-side along the margin. Brownish sporangia are seen emerging from the top of the light-yellow indusia.*

25b – A patch of **Davallia triphylla** *growing on a boulder in a lowland forest.*

26a – **Dicranopteris curranii** *is closely related to* D. linearis *but has slightly wider frond blades. Its spores have a single, elongated scar, whereas those of* D. linearis *have a three-pointed scar. The picture here shows the paired branching of the fronds.*

26a▼

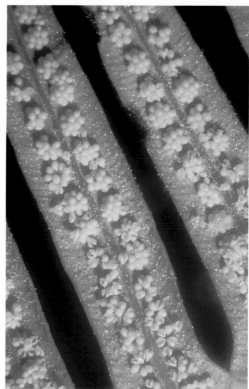

26b▲

26c▲   26d▼

26b – The slender creeping rhizomes of **Dicranopteris** *on the surface of the soil, with crosiers of young fronds at intervals. Because the rhizomes are superficial, firing is one way of destroying the thicket.*

26c – Clumps of sori on the under surface of frond lobes. Unlike the sporangia of other ferns, those of **Dicranopteris** *split open at the top into two halves. The characteristic band of annulus around each sporangium is not present here. The yellow dots all over the surface of the frond lobes are spores.*

26d – **Dicranopteris linearis** *var.* **subpectinata** *does not form thickets. It has alternate, unequal forking of the fronds and scrambles up trees along the edge of the forest.*

27a – The fronds of **Dipteris conjugata,** *each made up of two fan-shaped halves on a long stalk. Each half is divided into a number of lobes. The frond on the right has just unfolded, as its tips are still tinged red.*

27 – Dipteris conjugata

For a long time, this was believed to be a mountain fern, growing at an altitude of around 600–1,500 metres. However, it has recently been observed in Endau-Rompin in Malaysia at much lower altitudes. In Singapore and parts of southern Johore, the plant has been recorded on coastal cliffs. This has led to speculation that these cliffs were at a higher altitude during the Pleistocene era than they are today. With the temperature then much lower than it is currently, spores of this fern were able to germinate and develop thickets. The fact that no young plants are found in these low-lying areas, together with the slow deterioration of these fern communities, lends some credibility to the theory. On mountain tops where the light is not filtered by trees, this fern may form small patches of pure stands.

27a▼

Cultivation: A well-drained acid soil, light shade and plenty of water are essential. Although it needs a cool climate for its growth, it can be grown in the lowland of the tropics. Established plants should not be disturbed unnecessarily.

28 – *Dipteris lobbiana*

This lowland rainforest fern grows along the banks of rivers and streams, sometimes to an altitude of 1,000 metres. It also grows on rocks in stream beds, as long as there is a break in the forest canopy to let in light. The structure of the frond is similar to the mountain *D. conjugata*, but the fronds are much smaller and each lobe is very narrow. The narrowness of the frond lobes adapts the plant to a life near rivers, especially those subject to sudden flooding.

29 – *Doryopteris ludens*

This fern is very attractive because of its thick, leathery fronds, which are simple but lobed. The veins on the undersurface of the fronds are shiny and black. The fertile fronds have a much longer stalk and are larger and more deeply dissected than the sterile fronds. Sori are continuous along the margin of the frond lobes. This lowland rainforest fern is found in the limestone hills of Malaysia. *Cultivation:* Can be grown in coral rockeries under shade. Potted, the soil should be well-drained and alkaline.

27b – A sparse thicket of **Dipteris** *together with* Gleichenia *at the mountain resort of Fraser's Hill, Peninsular Malaysia.*

28 – **Dipteris lobbiana**.

29 – **Doryopteris ludens**.

27b▼

28▲   29▼

30 – *Drynaria quercifolia*

The **Oak-leaf Fern** is an epiphyte of lowland rainforest, secondary forest, rubber plantations, urban areas and wayside trees. It is a less efficient litter collector than the Bird's-nest Fern or the Staghorn Fern. The broad, unstalked nest fronds often overlap along the thick rhizome. They are persistent, turning brown with age but not falling. These nest fronds offer a covering for the rhizome and trap whatever falling leaves they can between the fronds and the surface of the branch. The foliage fronds are longer, stalked and deeply lobed. They bear the sporangia. With age, segments of the blade fall off, eventually leaving only the main brown stalk sticking out of the rhizome. *D. sparsisora* is another species commonly found in the lowlands, but it has much smaller fronds.

Cultivation: Pieces of the thick rhizome can be planted in soil or attached to slabs of fern roots or even pieces of wood and kept under light shade. The plant grows best under warm and humid conditions but can tolerate cool temperatures. Established plants can be left for short periods under direct sun and days without watering.

30a – This old Rain Tree is heavily overgrown with **Oak-leaf Ferns**. *The prominent, deeply lobed foliage fronds totally cover the nest fronds, which are seen only on the vertical branch towards the centre right. Notice also a number of large Bird's-nest Ferns on this tree.*

30b – A young **Oak-leaf Fern**. *The early fronds of ferns are usually different in shape from the later, older fronds. Here, the early fronds are simple, unlobed structures.*

◀30a   30b▼

123

*30c – **Oak-leaf Ferns** growing along the trunk and branch of a forest tree. The closely overlapping, brown nest fronds and the sparsely spaced, stalked foliage fronds are clearly seen in this picture.*

30d – The undersurface of a fertile frond lobe showing the rounded sori arranged in regular rows on each side of the main vein.

*30e – An **Oak-leaf Fern** grown on a piece of wood, showing how the foliage fronds assist in the channelling of falling leaves into the space created by the nest fronds.*

◄30c   30d▲   30e▼

31▲   32a▼

31 – *Drynaria rigidula*

Related to the Oak-leaf Fern of the lowlands, *Drynaria rigidula* is a common epiphyte of mountain forests that grows on old trees and even on rocky outcrops. The foliage fronds of this species are pinnate compound, unlike the simple lobed fronds of the Oak-Leaf Fern. The sori are arranged in a single row on either side of the pinna. Like its lowland relative, the nest fronds are persistent and remain on the plant as brown structures for a long time to assist in litter collection. The foliage fronds shed their pinnae individually until only the central stalks are left as black projections. *Cultivation:* Portions of the rhizome with fronds can be rooted onto fern root slabs or pieces of Tree Fern stem, using sphagnum moss or coconut fibres to encourage root growth. Leave the plants under shade and water regularly until they are well established. Although it grows well under cool conditions, it can survive in the warm tropical lowlands. In baskets, it needs a well-drained coarse mixture.

32b▲

32 – *Gleichenia truncata*

This fern forms thickets in open places at high elevations. It is also seen in lowlands, scrambling up vegetation at the forest edge, or growing in isolation in open areas together with *Dicranopteris*. The fronds are forked up to four or more times. Each branch is leafy with narrow lobes.
Cultivation: Pieces of the rhizome can be grown in clay or a mixture of clay and loam. The plant needs plenty of water and can tolerate light shade to full sun. It can be grown under warm to cool conditions.

31 – **Drynaria rigidula**.

32a – A single frond of **Gleichenia truncata** *forking repeatedly. Note the dark brown frond stalk rising vertically from the ground to give rise to the first pair of short, leafless branches. At the tip of the stalk is the dormant apical bud covered with a pair of leafy protective structures.*

32b – A thicket of **Gleichenia truncata** *in an open area at Fraser's Hill, Peninsular Malaysia. The black patches between the greenness of the fern are the old, dead fronds.*

33 – *Goniophlebium percussum*

This is a common epiphytic fern that grows on old trees in lowland, mountain and secondary forests and oil palm plantations, as long as there is sufficient light. It has large, pinnate compound fronds of up to 1.5 metres long, which hang down conspicuously from the host tree. The oppositely arranged pinnae bear a row of roundish sori on either side of the midrib. The sori are sunk in cavities that appear as small papillae on the upper surface.

Cultivation: Pieces of the rhizome can be planted in a well-drained soil or attached to coconut fibres on a branch of a tree and watered regularly until roots are established. The plant should be left under light shade in warm locations. It can also tolerate cooler conditions.

34 – *Heterogonium sagenoides*

This is a large ground fern of lowland and mountain forests. The large, pinnate compound fronds are light green and soft-textured, making the fern easy to recognise in the forest. Pinnae are deeply lobed and the sori are borne in a row along each side of the main vein of the pinna lobe.

Cultivation: This fern can be grown under warm to cool conditions in well-drained, organic-rich soil. It needs shade and plenty of water.

33a▲   33b▼   34 ▶

33a – A number of large **Goniophlebium percussum** *fronds hanging gracefully from the trunk of an old oil palm.*

33b – The undersurface of a fertile **Goniophlebium percussum** *frond showing the two rows of brown sori along each pinna.*

34 – **Heterogonium sagenoides**.

35 – *Histiopteris stipulacea*

This mountain fern is abundant at the forest edge, where it sometimes forms thickets. The fronds are very large, twice pinnate to thrice pinnate compound, and the apex continues to elongate for some time. The dark, shiny frond stalk bears pairs of opposite pinnae. Each pinna bears a few pairs of opposite pinnules. The terminal pinnule is lobed at the base.

Cultivation: This fern grows best under cool and moist conditions, either in the ground or in a pot with well-drained, organic-rich soil.

36 – *Hymenophyllum* and *Trichomanes*

These are the **Filmy Ferns** commonly found in mossy forests in the highlands, growing on bryophyte-covered tree trunks, branches and rocks. They are also found in the lowlands where there is plenty of shade and moisture.

Cultivation: Depending on the species, plants can be planted in soil or on various media for epiphytes, in light to deep shade, and in cool to warm conditions. These ferns need a high moisture level to survive.

---

35 – **Histiopteris stipulacea**.

36a – The pendulous fronds of **Hymenophyllum serrulatum** *growing on the lower trunk of a tree in mountain forest. The fern is wet with moisture and the fronds appear light green and glistening.*

36b – A patch of **Hymenophyllum** *growing under deep shade at 1,700 metres in the Cameron Highlands, Malaysia. The fronds have developed a bluish sheen as a result of the shade.*

35▼

36a▲ 36b▼

36c – **Trichomanes** *differs from* Hymenophyllum *in the indusium. The* Trichomanes *indusium is trumpet-shaped. The spores are borne on an elongated hair-like structure which sticks out prominently from the indusium mouth. The indusium of* Hymenophyllum *is two-lipped and the hair-like structure does not stick out prominently.*

36d – *An erect* **Trichomanes** *sp. with pinnate compound fronds.*

37a – *A rotting piece of old* **Lecanopteris carnosa** *rhizome lying on the forest floor. There are a number of small, living rhizome patches still with fronds.*

37b – *A colony of* **Lecanopteris carnosa** *with the crusty rhizome growing completely round the branch of the host tree. The old, knobby rhizome has turned black, while the living portions are still green. Fronds are deeply lobed, with the stalk arising from a mound of rhizome.*

37 – *Lecanopteris carnosa*

This fern grows on old trees at altitudes of around 1,000–2,000 metres. The fleshy rhizome forms a thick crust around the branch of the tree, and numerous ants live within the hollow interior, turning the fern into a living ants' nest. These ants bring small seeds to their nest which may germinate and grow out of crevices in the rhizome.

Cultivation: Plants do not survive well when the crusty stem is forcefully detached from the tree on which it is growing. However, when the plant is removed intact with part of the tree branch, the possibility of surviving increases. It needs damp and cool conditions to grow, but it has been known to survive in the tropical lowlands when kept shaded and well watered.

36c▼

36d▼

37a▲   37b▼

38a – **Lecanopteris sinuosa** *makes an attractive ornamental plant when grown on a piece of fern root. Most of the fronds here are fertile, with a single row of rounded sori on each side of the midrib.*

38b – **Lecanopteris sinuosa** *on the bark of a Rain Tree along an expressway in Singapore.*

39 – **Lindsaea ensifolia**.

38a▲   38b▼

38 – *Lecanopteris sinuosa*

Previously known as *Phymatodes sinuosa*, this ant fern grows on trees in moderately exposed places. Its creeping rhizome is covered with a layer of overlapping scales, giving it the appearance of a snake. The rhizome is flattened and hollow, and masses of ants live within this space. The simple, stalked fronds fall off when old, leaving behind small stumps all over the rhizome. The sporangia are grouped in oval sori arranged in a single row on each side of the midrib. This fern is often found growing together with *Dischidia major*, a non-fern with specially hollowed leaves to accommodate ants inside.

Cultivation: The tangled rhizomes can be grown on fern root slabs if given warm, shaded and damp conditions.

39 – *Lindsaea ensifolia*

This *Lindsaea* is a smallish lowland fern that grows on the forest floor under slightly open conditions. It is also found in urban areas on earth banks where there is sufficient shade. The frond is pinnate compound with about four pairs of narrow pinnae and a terminal pinna. It is easily recognised as a *Lindsaea* by its continuous sorus along the pinna margin covered by a narrow indusium which opens towards the margin. Young plants have simple fronds.

Cultivation: This fern grows well in well-drained soil with plenty of humus. Keep it away from the direct sun. It tolerates cool to warm conditions.

39▼

40 – *Lindsaea parasitica*

This is an attractive plant of the lowland rainforest. It has pinnate compound fronds when young and twice pinnate fronds when old. Pinnules are crescent shaped, slightly overlapping, and arranged on both sides of the stalk. When fertile, the sorus is continuous along the upper margin of the pinnule. The plant has a long and thin rhizome that climbs up the base of trees and sometimes up rock surfaces.

*Cultivation:*Plant in a well-drained soil with plenty of humus and place under shade. The plant can tolerate cool to warm conditions.

41 – *Lindsaea rigida*

This mountain species is closely related to the lowland *L. parasitica*. It grows on the ground or on fallen trees among mosses. Fronds are twice pinnate compound with the pinnules widely spaced and the upper margin shallowly lobed. The plant is just as attractive as the lowland species.

42 – *Lycopodium*

This **Clubmoss** has erect fertile branches, each with a long cone at the end. Clubmosses of many species are common in mountain forests. They grow from the ground between dwarfed trees or from the branches of trees, or climb up trees.

◀ 40   41▲   42▼

---

40 – **Lindsaea parasitica**.

41 – **Lindsaea rigida**.

42 – **Lycopodium**.

43a▲   43b▼

138

43 – *Lygodium flexuosum*

This is a climbing fern common in open locations in the lowlands. It has an underground rhizome which gives out compound fronds at intervals. The pinnae are borne along a slender "stalk" that keeps on elongating, sometimes reaching 2 metres or longer. The fronds twine around supports as they elongate. *Cultivation:* Pieces of the underground rhizome need to be dug out of the ground and planted in clayey to loamy soil under light shade to full sun.

43c▲   44a▼

44 – *Marsilea crenata*

The **Water Clover** or Water Shamrock is known to the Malays as *tapak itek*, meaning "duck's footstep". Its fronds consist of four leaflets that look like a four-leafed clover. This water fern is fairly common in rice fields. The slender rhizome establishes itself in the mud and gives out long-stalked fronds with the leaflets floating on the surface of the water. As the rice harvesting season approaches, the water level in the field is lowered and the fern produces smaller and shorter fronds. It only develops reproductive organs when the field is dry.

44b▼

43a – The climbing **Lygodium flexuosum** *twines round plants at the edge of a secondary forest.*

43b – A pair of **Lygodium flexuosum** *pinnae, each with a number of pinnules. The pinnules are fringed with narrow fertile lobes.*

43c – Fertile **Lygodium flexuosum** *lobes with two rows of large sporangia, each protected by a cup-shaped indusium.*

44a – **Water Clover** *growing in the muddy ground between rice plants in Indonesia.*

44b – A close-up of **Water Clover**.

45▲   46a▼

45 – *Matonia pectinata*

Matonia pectinata, native to the Malay Peninsular and Borneo, is a very primitive fern. On the basis of fossil evidence, this species is considered to be the sole surviving member of an ancient genus. It is confined to exposed ridges and mountain tops, where it forms thickets. Its fronds have long, erect stalks that fork at the tip, each branching many times in a peculiarly unequal fashion to give rise to a fan-shaped structure.
Cultivation: The plant prefers acidic soil and cool conditions.

46 – *Mesophlebion chlamydophorum*

This fern grows in freshwater swamps and lowland and mountain forests. The fronds are pinnate compound, with about 15 pairs of deeply-lobed pinnae.

47 – *Microlepia speluncae*

This is a fairly large ground fern of the lowland rainforest. Fronds are usually twice pinnate compound, although the larger fronds may be thrice pinnate. The pinnae are deeply lobed, and sori are found at the base of the sinuses between the lobes, each with a indusium.
Cultivation: Plants can be grown in well-drained soil and kept under shade in warm to cool conditions.

---

45 – **Matonia pectinata**.

46a – A handsome patch of **Mesophlebion chlamydophorum** *growing at the Singapore Botanic Gardens.*

46b – The undersurface of a pinna of **Mesophlebion chlamydophorum**, *showing the rounded sori.*

47 – **Microlepia speluncae**.

46b▼

47▼

48 – *Microsorum punctatum*

This is a common epiphyte of open areas. It sometimes grows on walls. It is easily mistaken for the Bird's-nest Fern because of its strap-shaped fronds; however, it does not form a symmetrical nest. It has a creeping rhizome and small groups of sori scattered irregularly over the upper half of the frond.

Cultivation: Plants can be attached to tree branches, potted, or grown in hanging baskets. The soil should be coarse and well-drained. The plant needs light shade, warmth and plenty of moisture.

49 – *Nephrolepis acutifolia*

Closely allied to *N. biserrata*, which is a ground fern of open places, this is an epiphyte of old trees in the lowlands. Its slender, creeping rhizome adheres closely to the tree trunk and branches. Unlike other species of the genus, which have round sori, the sorus here is marginal and elongated.

Cultivation: Plants can be attached to fern root slabs and left under light shade in warm locations. When potted, a well-drained soil is needed. The plant should be watered regularly. It is sensitive to the cold.

---

48 – **Microsorum punctatum**. *The plant growing on the bark of the tree with small, fleshy and oppositely arranged leaves is* Dischidia nummularia, *an ant plant.*

49 – *This* **Nephrolepis acutifolia** *is growing on a Rain Tree. Its narrow, pinnate fronds dangle gracefully from the branches. It spreads to other parts of the tree with the help of its slender runners.*

48▼
49 ▶

50a▲   50b▼   51a▲

144

50 – *Nephrolepis biserrata*

A very common lowland fern of open places, *Nephrolepis biserrata* can overrun an area within a short time with the help of its many wiry runners. The runners grow from the short, erect stem, each giving rise to one or more plantlets some distance away from the parent plant. The pinnate compound fronds are erect, with the pinnae arranged at right angles to the axis. The indusia are kidney-shaped.

Cultivation: Plantlets developing from runners can be planted in any type of soil, as long as it is well-drained. It needs light shade and plenty of water. This is a hardy fern.

51 – *Oleandra pistillaris*

This straggling plant is a thicket-forming fern that grows in mountain forests. It is easily mistaken for a flowering plant because of its simple fronds, which are borne in rosettes at unequal intervals along the stiff, erect stem. The fertile fronds bear a single row of sori on each side of the midrib.

50a – A thicket of **Nephrolepis biserrata** *with the tufted, erect pinnate compound fronds.*

50b – **Nephrolepis** *is sometimes found growing on old walls. The plants here have many runners growing from the base of the plant and spreading all over the retaining wall.*

51a – A fertile **Oleandra pistillaris** *frond with a row of sori on each side of the midrib.*

51b – The shrubby habit of **Oleandra pistillaris** *can be seen at a forest edge, where it is growing among* Gleichenia.

51b▼

52 – *Ophioglossum pendulum*

Hanging Adder's-tongue Ferns can only develop within the nests of the Staghorn or the Bird's-nest Fern. When the spores land in the nest, they germinate among the decaying leaves and wait for a specific fungus to infect them. Without the fungus, the germinating spores cannot develop as they are not able to manufacture food in the dark. The prothalli take several years to develop and produce sexual organs. If fertilisation occurs, a young Adder's-tongue Fern develops. Initially, this young fern has to depend on the prothallus and its fungus for survival. Only when its first frond emerges from the nest and turns green can the plant survive independently.

Cultivation: Plants can be removed from the host fern with the roots intact and grown independently using fern roots, sphagnum moss or coconut fibres as the medium. Keep warm, shaded and damp at all times.

52a▲   52b▼

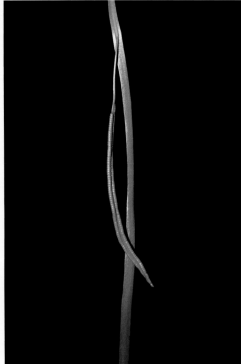

*52a – Narrow fronds of the **Adder's-tongue Fern** emerging from the nest of an old Staghorn Fern. One of the fronds to the right bears a fertile lobe.*

*52b – A single frond of **Adder's-tongue Fern** with a fertile lobe attached near its base. This fertile lobe consists of many rounded sporangia fused together. When the sporangia mature, they split to allow the numerous yellow spores to be liberated.*

*52c – Longitudinal section of an **Adder's-tongue Fern** root showing the cells infected with fungal mycelium, stained blue to make them more apparent.*

53 – *Ophioglossum reticulatum*

This **Adder's-tongue Fern** is found in poor soil under rather open conditions, from urban sites to the sides of tarred roads in mountainous areas. The fleshy and rather extensive roots produce root buds at intervals, which develop into new plants. Only one or two fronds develop at a time. When fertile, the simple frond bears a long spike with a tip resembling the tongue of an adder, hence the common name. The plant is eaten as a vegetable.

Cultivation: Plants can be dug out of the ground and planted in well-drained, loamy soil under shade. It needs plenty of organic matter and water and tolerates cool to warm conditions.

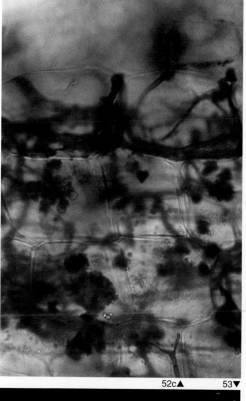

53 – **Ophioglossum reticulatum**.

52c▲   53▼

54 – *Photinopteris speciosa*

In northern Peninsular Malaysia, this fern grows at high altitudes in the crowns of old trees and on exposed rocks and old walls. Towards the south, it grows on old mangrove trees by rivers. The pinnate compound fronds resemble the leaves of flowering plants and can be easily mistaken for them unless they are fertile. Fertile fronds are easily recognised as belonging to a fern—although the lower pinnae are normal, the upper pinnae are very narrow and bear the sporangia.

---

54 – **Photinopteris speciosa**.

55 – **Phymatopteris triloba**.

◀54   55▼

55 – *Phymatopteris triloba*

This is a fairly common epiphyte of mountain forests. The fronds are dimorphous, the sterile having three lobes and the fertile up to four pairs. The lobes of the fertile fronds are narrower, with the sori arranged in a single row on each side of the midrib. The almost round sori are sunk into the frond blade, appearing as small knobs on the upper surface.

Cultivation: Plants can be induced to root with moist sphagnum moss and attached to various media suitable for epiphytes. They should be grown under cool, moist and shaded conditions.

56 – *Phymatosorus scolopendria*

This creeping epiphytic fern is common on lowland trees in open places. The shape of the fronds varies from simple and unlobed to those with three or four pairs of lobes. The fertile fronds are dotted with two irregular rows of sori on either side of the midrib of each lobe. The round to oval sori are sunk into the frond blade such that the upper surface is prominently raised. The Malays call it *paku wangi*, meaning "fragrant fern", and sometimes use it to perfume their clothes and to scent coconut oil. The fragrance comes from the presence of coumarin, a vanilla-scented crystalline ester.

Cultivation: Pieces of the rhizome can be propagated in well-drained soil or attached to a fern root slab. Plants should be kept under light shade and in a warm location.

56a▼   56b▼   56c ▶

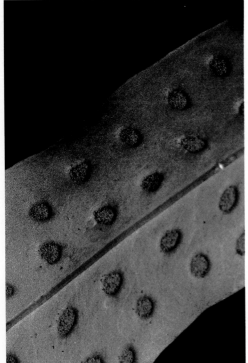

56a – A dense patch of **Phymatosorus scolopendria** *growing on the surface of large boulders along the coast in Malaysia.*

56b – The undersurface of a fertile frond lobe of **Phymatosorus scolopendria***, showing the two rows of sunken sori.*

56c – A patch of **Phymatosorus scolopendria** *growing from the fork of a Rain Tree. Notice the fertile and sterile fronds and the green rhizomes. In the background on the left are Pigeon Orchids* (Dendrobium crumenatum)*, a common epiphyte.*

57 – *Pityrogramma calomelanos*

The **Silver Fern** originates from tropical America. Introduced to Asia as an ornamental fern, it has spread as a weed throughout the tropics. It is common on disturbed ground, in gardens, by the roadside, and in rural areas. In fact, it follows people, appearing wherever there is human activity.

Cultivation: This fern is easy to grow and tolerates most soil types and a wide range of temperatures. It needs plenty of light.

*57a – The undersurface of the **Silver Fern** is silvery due to the presence of a waxy powder. The round structures are young (green) and old (black) sporangia. The annulus can be clearly seen in the older sporangia.*

*57b – The **Silver Fern** growing together with* Nephrolepis biserrata. *The highly attractive frond is twice pinnate compound.*

57a▲   57b▼

58 – *Platycerium coronarium*

The **Disc Staghorn Fern** is a common epiphyte of urban and forest trees. It is the most efficient of the litter-collecting ferns. The large nest fronds grow upwards to enclose the short rhizome and roots as well as to wrap themselves around the supporting branch. They form a large nest to accumulate falling leaves from the host tree, which slowly rot inside. As the nest fronds age, they turn brown and curl inwards into the nest to contribute to the organic matter inside. At the same time these dying fronds help to keep the accumulated leaves in the nest in place. The fern also bears normal foliage fronds, which hang down from the nest. These narrow, branched foliage fronds do not contribute to the organic matter of the nest but fall off when old. The upper portions of some pendulous fronds develop semicircular fertile structures, the undersurfaces of which are covered with a dense layer of sporangia.

*Cultivation:*Small nests can be attached to wooden blocks to be hung indoors or outdoors, always away from the direct rays of the sun. Nests can also be

58a▲   58b▼

58a– A single foliage frond of **Platycerium coronarium** *showing the short bifurcating lobes at the top and the pendulous longer bifurcating lobes. The semicircular fertile lobe is attached below the upper lobes. Its undersurface is brown due to the presence of tightly packed sporangia and sterile hairs. This brown mass loosens as the sporangia mature.*

58b – A large nest of **Platycerium coronarium**. *The original plant has produced a number of side shoots, resulting in more than one growing point, each with its own nest fronds and hanging foliage fronds.*

attached to the branches of trees. Water them regularly until they are well established. There is no need to apply fertilisers as long as the nests collect dead leaves from surrounding trees. Plants can tolerate cool to warm conditions but are very cold-sensitive.

59 – *Platycerium holttumii*

Holttum's Staghorn Fern is an epiphyte that grows on tall trees in lowland rainforest and mountain forest. The nest is similar to that of the Disc Staghorn but is sometimes much larger. The foliage frond is wedge-shaped, with two main lobes, each branching further to form narrow and forked lobes. The fertile portion is found on the undersurface of the sinus of each of the two main lobes. *Cultivation:* Large nests can be grown successfully if placed under light shade and watered infrequently. This fern

prefers cool conditions but can tolerate warm conditions. It is cold-sensitive.

58c – A sporeling of **Platycerium coronarium** *growing from the trunk of a Rain Tree. The first few fronds have only managed to provide a cover for the roots. Foliage fronds have yet to develop. It will be some time before normal nest fronds are formed to accumulate a large enough supply of organic matter to ensure a constant supply of nutrients and moisture for its growth. In the meantime the young plant is highly susceptible to drying. Note the presence of bryophytes and a Dragon's-scale Fern. The successful establishment of this sporeling has no doubt been due to the presence of these bryophytes, which have shared moisture and nutrients from the organic matter held by their roots.*

59 – **Platycerium holttumii**. *The brown patch on the pendulous foliage frond is the layer of sporangia.*

58c▼   59 ▶

60 – *Platycerium ridleyi*

Ridley's Staghorn Fern is found only on lowland forest trees, often by rivers. Unlike the more common Disc Staghorn, it is not found in open country. The plant is much smaller and the nest fronds are strongly ribbed, enclosing the rhizome and roots in a semicircular mound. Numerous ants live within the nest. Foliage fronds grow from the centre of the nest, arching upwards and repeatedly branching. Spores are found on special spoon-shaped lobes.

Cultivation: Nests can be attached to fern root slabs or pieces of wood, with sphagnum moss in between to provide the organic matter for water retention and nutrient supply. The plants need a warm and reasonably shaded location and a constant supply of organic matter within the nest fronds; otherwise, organic fertilisers need to be supplied.

This species is very sensitive to cold and is suited only to the tropics.

61 – *Pronephrium triphyllum*

This is a lowland ground fern found under light shade. It has become rather weedy, growing in rubber and oil palm plantations and in grassy areas. The fern is easily recognised by its trifoliate fronds on erect stalks, the lateral pinnae opposite and slightly below the terminal pinna. The fertile frond has a longer stalk and narrower pinnae and stands way above the sterile fronds.

Cultivation: Plants grow well under light shade in a variety of soil types, as long as drainage is good.

---

60 – **Platycerium ridleyi** *plants grown by a private collector in Singapore.*

61 – **Pronephrium triphyllum**.

60▼   61 ▶

62a – A thicket of Bracken (Pteridium aquilinum) in the Cameron Highlands, Peninsular Malaysia. Note the many erect frond stalks rising from the underground rhizome, each bearing a few pairs of pinnae. This is probably a new growth after a fire, as the fronds are still elongating, with uniform growth.

62b – The undersurface of fertile Pteridium aquilinum pinnules, showing the deeply dissected lobes. The sori are marginal along the lobes and are protected by a narrow indusium. The midvein of the pinnules, as well as the stalk bearing the pinnae, are covered with hairs.

63a – Mature Pteris ensiformis plants with narrow pinnae, the lower pair with a side branch.

62a▲   62b▼

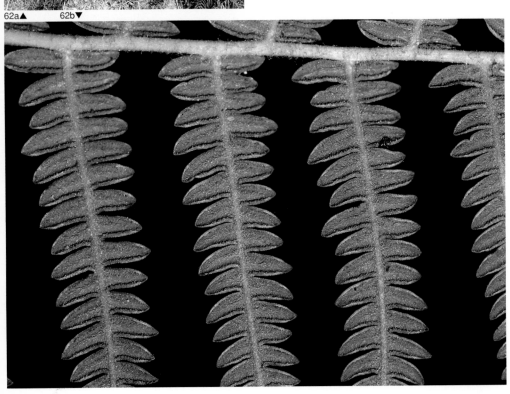

62 – *Pteridium aquilinum*

Bracken is found widely throughout the temperate and tropical regions of the world. It forms thickets in both highland and lowland regions. Its thrice pinnate compound fronds continue to elongate for a considerable period of time, giving out paired pinnae bearing deeply lobed pinnules. Thickets of bracken are not easily destroyed by fire as the plant has an underground rhizome.

Cultivation: Bracken is generally difficult to transplant, but young, actively growing rhizome tips can sometimes be successfully rooted in pots, to be transplanted out. It needs a well-drained soil and plenty of sun. Plants can tolerate warm to cold conditions.

63 – *Pteris ensiformis*

This fertile ground fern of open locations can easily be mistaken for *Lindsaea ensifolia*. The pinnate compound frond with narrow, oppositely arranged pinnae as well as the terminal pinna and marginal sorus look very like those of *L. ensifolia*. However, the lower pinnae usually have a short lobe or a pair of lobes near the base. Also, the indusium covering the sorus opens away from the pinna margin. The sterile fronds of this fern are distinctly different from the fertile fronds—the sterile frond is shorter, the pinnae broader, and some of the pinnae develop pinnules.

Cultivation: Pteris ensiformis makes an attractive pot plant, especially the var. *Victoriae*. The plant needs well-drained soil and can tolerate the full sun for part of the day.

63a▼

63b▲

63c▲ 64a▼

64 – *Pteris vittata*

This is a common fern of the tropics and subtropics, often seen in urban locations, such as on drains and old walls. It also grows in open grounds in the lowlands and sometimes in the mountains as well. The pinnate fronds can be a long as 1 metre, with each pinna up to about 1 cm wide. The short basal pinnae increase in length upwards, ending in a long terminal pinna. Sori are linear and are located along the margin of the pinna, with the indusium opening inwards.

Cultivation: This plant is easily grown in a free-draining medium of most soil types. It tolerates strong light, short drying periods and cold to warm conditions.

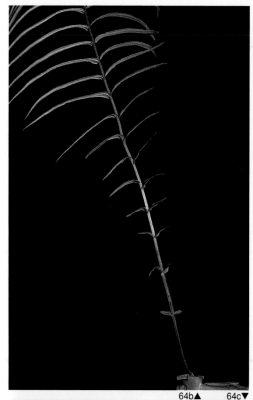

64b▲   64c▼

63b – Young **Pteris ensiformis** *plants with wider fronds and rounded pinnae, some of which have developed pinnules.*

63c – **Pteris ensiformis** *var.* **Victoriae** *was probably a mutant that was selected as an horticultural plant. It now sometimes grows wild in urban locations.*

64a – A patch of **Pteris vittata** *growing from the ledge of a building in the older section of Singapore.*

64b – A single frond of **Pteris vittata** *showing the arrangement of the pinnae. Note that the lowest pinnae are barely developed.*

64c – A segment of a fertile pinna of **Pteris vittata** *showing the linear sorus along both edges.*

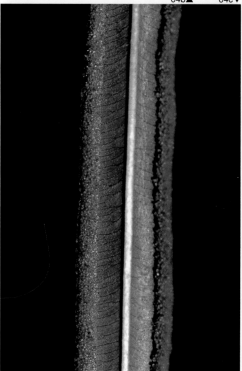

65 – *Pyrrosia floccigera*

This *Pyrrosia*, unlike its lowland relatives, thrives best in exposed places in mountain forest up to an altitude of about 1,500 metres. Fronds are simple, stalked and narrow, tapering at both ends. The surface of the frond is covered with a loose, star-shaped mass of hairs. With maturity, the upper surface loses these hairs but the lower-surface retains them, appearing light brown. Fertile fronds are covered with numerous, rounded sori on both sides of the midrib, causing them to appear rust brown.

Cultivation: Pieces of rhizomes with fronds can be attached to various media suitable for epiphytes and grown under cool, moist and shaded conditions.

66 – *Pyrrosia lanceolata*

This is an epiphytic fern of roadside trees, closely allied to but less common than *Pyrrosia longifolia* and *P. piloselloides*. It has much shorter sterile fronds than *P. longifolia*. The sporangia on the fertile fronds are in rounded sori, arranged in marginal bands confined to the upper third of the frond.

Cultivation: Reasonably long pieces of rhizome can be wrapped in sphagnum moss or coconut fibres and watered regularly to induce rooting. Once the roots are well established, the plant can be left under light shade in a warm location and kept moist by watering once in a while.

---

65 – **Pyrrosia floccigera**.

66 – **Pyrrosia lanceolata**.

◀65   66▼

67 – *Pyrrosia longifolia*

Pyrrosia longifolia is a common epiphyte of trees in open places. The long, narrow fronds, sometimes growing up to 1 metre long, hang down in bunches from the trunk and branches of trees.

Cultivation: Pieces of rhizome with fronds can be grown on slabs of fern roots. The plant needs light shade and moist, warm conditions.

68 – *Pyrrosia piloselloides*

The **Dragon's-scale Fern** is a pioneer of epiphytic ferns on roadside trees. It is usually the first to appear, growing at the angle between the branches and the trunk, in the channel where rain water flows down the trunk from the crown of the tree. The thick, oval fronds store water to tide the fern through periods of drought. Fertile fronds are long and narrow.

Cultivation: Pieces of rhizome can be grown on slabs of fern roots or the branches of trees. The plant needs light shade and moist, warm conditions.

67a▲   67b▼   68a ▶

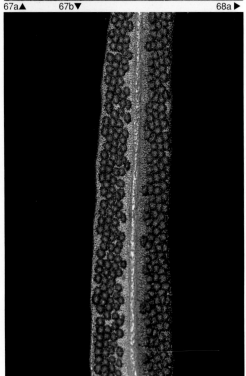

67a – A thick growth of **Pyrrosia longifolia** *growing from the left side of the Mexican Lilac Tree* (Gliricidia sepium*). The tree is usually covered with this fern and the Dragon's-scale Fern* (P. piloselloides*).

67b – The undersurface of a **Pyrrosia longifolia** *frond showing the roundish, brown sori closely scattered over the upper third of the frond. The conspicuous darker brown ring around each sorus is the older sporangia. The greyish layer between the sori are the star-shaped hairs which cover the frond's undersurface.*

68a – Sometimes, the fertile frond of the **Dragon's-scale Fern** *forks, as seen in this picture.*

164

*68b – The fork of a Yellow Flame Tree with a thick patch of **Dragon's-scale Fern**. Longer fertile fronds can be seen among the oval, sterile fronds.*

*68c – Coconut palms are commonly overgrown with **Dragon's-scale Ferns**, as the many cracks on the trunk of the palm provide a moist environment for the spores to germinate and develop though the prothallus stage. Note the many fertile fronds, as well as a young Bird's-nest Fern halfway up the trunk.*

*68d – Close-up of a fertile frond of **Dragon's-scale Fern**, showing the thick band of sporangia along the frond's margin.*

*68e – Under conditions of heavy shade, the sterile fronds of the **Dragon's-scale Fern** lose their oval shape and become elongated. The fertile fronds become much longer. Note the brownish marginal band of sporangia around the fertile fronds.*

68b▲   68c▼   68d▼   68e▶

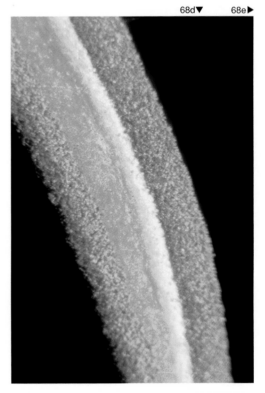

69 – *Quercifilix zeylanica*

This rock fern grows in lightly shaded locations in the lowland rainforest. The fronds are unusual in that they are trifoliate with a pair of small, rounded pinnae below the larger, shallow-lobed terminal pinna.

Cultivation: Plant in a shaded location in well-drained soil with plenty of humus. The fern needs regular watering and warm conditions to grow.

70 – *Salvinia molesta*

The **Water Spangle** is a free-floating water fern of freshwater ponds, streams, reservoirs and rice fields. The plant fragments easily, and this helps it to multiply. The fronds are in threes, two of which are normal and green. These are simple structures, floating on the surface of the water and covered with a layer of egg-beater type hairs. The third frond is modified into rootlike structures and is submerged in the water.

69▲   70a▼

*69 – **Quercifilix zeylanica**. The two fertile fronds are distinctly different from the sterile fronds, having a longer stalk and a very much reduced surface area.*

*70a – Close-up of **Water Spangle**. The surface of these fronds is covered with hairs to help keep the fronds afloat.*

*70b – Close-up of the egg-beater type of hairs on the surface of the **Water Spangle** frond.*

*70c – This 1978 picture shows **Water Spangle** proliferating in Seletar Reservoir in Singapore. It was introduced into Singapore as an ornamental plant, but over the years it escaped into ponds and finally found its way into the country's reservoir. Because its presence can have an adverse effect on the quality of the potable water, thousands of dollars were spent to remove it.*

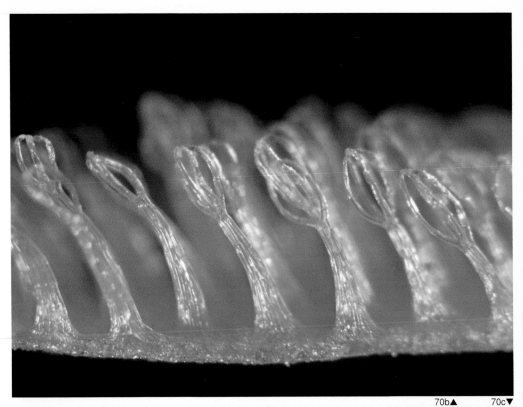

70b▲   70c▼

71 – *Schizaea dichotoma*

This is an uncommon **Grass Fern** found in open forest in the lowlands, sometimes to an altitude of 1,000 metres. Its repeatedly forked fronds make it rather attractive.

---

71 – A top view of the fronds of **Schizaea dichotoma**, *with the branches ending in short, brown fertile lobes.*

72 – **Sphenomeris chinensis**.

72 – *Sphenomeris chinensis*

The **Chinese Lace Fern** is an attractive fern with finely dissected fronds. It occurs in lowland and mountain forests, on earth banks, by roadsides and by streams. Sori are located at the end of the frond divisions, each enclosed within an indusium.

Cultivation: The plant grows well in pots as long as it is shaded. It needs a well-drained soil and adequate watering. It tolerates cool to warm conditions.

◀71   72▼

73 – *Stenochlaena palustris*

This is the most common fern in freshwater swamps and in areas where the soil is wet and soggy. The plant scrambles up trees and sometimes forms thickets. The young fronds are pinkish and are eaten as a vegetable. The sterile fronds have broad pinnae. The pinnae of the fertile fronds are very much reduced, and the lower surface is covered with sporangia.

Cultivation: Plants are easily grown in the hot and wet tropics, provided there is sufficient water and sunlight.

74 – *Taenitis dimorpha*

This is a mid-mountain species growing under light shade. Sterile fronds are simple and are borne on a short stalk. Fertile fronds are pinnate compound, with one to four pairs of pinnae and a terminal pinna. The stalk of fertile fronds is much longer and the pinnae narrower. Sori are found in narrow bands between the midrib and the edge of the pinnae.

Cultivation: The plant needs well-drained soil, light shade and cool to warm conditions.

73▲ 74a▼ 74b ▶

---

73 – **Stenochlaena palustris**.

74a – **Taenitis dimorpha** *growing in the heath forest in Endau-Rompin, Peninsular Malaysia. The single fertile frond, with its very narrow pinnae and long, black stalk, is conspicuous.*

74b – **Taenitis blechnoides** *is usually associated with* T. dimorpha *and is found in the lowlands. Unlike* T. dimorpha, *the sterile fronds of* T. blechnoides *are pinnate compound. In this picture, one of the fertile pinnae has been twisted to show the two parallel rows of brown sori on either side of the midrib of the pinnae.*

75 – *Tectaria singaporeana*

The simple fronds of this ground fern make the plant easily mistaken for a flowering plant. However, the fertile fronds, which are narrower and longer than the sterile fronds, identify it as a fern. This fern is common on the forest floor in the lowlands.

Cultivation: Clumps of plants can be transplanted in pots with plenty of humus in well-drained soil. Plants need shade and plenty of water to survive.

75a – A fertile frond of **Tectaria singaporeana** *with numerous sori in regular rows on each side of the main vein.*

75b – A small patch of **Tectaria singaporeana** *with an erect young frond, which is slightly tinged with red. The longer frond to its right is a fertile frond. Its undersurface is covered with brown sori.*

75a▲   75b▼

76 – *Teratophyllum aculeatum*

This high-climbing fern starts life on the lowland forest floor. It creeps on the ground until it makes contact with the base of a tree or the side of a boulder, then it climbs upwards. The young plant bears fronds which are very different in shape and size from those of the adult. These are technically called bathyphylls, meaning "bottom fronds"—fronds found on the lower portion of the creeping stem. As the fern climbs higher, the fronds become larger, with distinctively larger pinnae. These are termed acrophylls or "top fronds". Only when the plant reaches the canopy of the forest will fertile fronds develop.

Cultivation: Properly dug out juvenile plants can be transplanted in humus-rich soil and grown under shade. They should be kept moist all the time until well established.

76a▲   76b▼

76a – The bathyphylls of **Teratophyllum aculeatum** *growing on a bryophyte-covered boulder in the forest in Pulau Tioman, Peninsular Malaysia. The shiny black rhizome bears two rows of attractive, pinnate compound fronds, the pinnae of which are deeply lobed.*

76b – The acrophylls of **Teratophyllum aculeatum** *at the top of the boulder. These are held away from the boulder and are also pinnate compound, but the pinnae look very different from those of the bathyphylls.*

76c – The bathyphylls of **Teratophyllum aculeatum** *growing up the stem of a young tree in the Bukit Timah forest in Singapore.*

77a – This **Shoestring Fern** *is growing profusely from the persistent leaf bases of old oil palms planted along the roadside.*

77b – A **Shoestring Fern** *growing on the trunk of a Rain Tree, between the roots of a Strangling Fig. The Shoestring Fern usually grows below a Bird's-nest Fern, benefiting from the excess water dripping down from the latter's nest.*

77c – A larger species, **Vittaria elongata***, is commonly found growing on oil palms. The fronds are occasionally branched at the stalk and are very much wider and longer, sometimes reaching 70 cm or longer.*

76c▲   77a▼

77 – *Vittaria ensiformis*

The **Shoestring Fern** is a common epiphyte of lowland trees. It is a smallish fern with simple, narrow fronds. The sorus is marginal, running along a groove formed by the reflexed edge of the frond.

Cultivation: Plants should be wrapped in coconut fibres or sphagnum moss, attached to a slab of fern root, and kept well watered. Keep in a warm location away from the direct sun.

77b▲   77c▼

GLOSSARY

acrophyll	Frond of adult ferns of the genera *Teratophyllum, Lomagramma* and *Lomariopsis*.
annulus	The row of thickened cells running round the sporangial head.
antheridium	The male sex organ in ferns, which produces sperms. (plural: antheridia)
archegonium	The female sex organ in ferns, which produces the egg. (plural: archegonia)
astringent	Causing contraction of body tissues; checking blood flow; restricting secretions of fluids.
auricle	Ear-like structure found at the base of the frond stalk of *Angiopteris* and *Marattia*.
bathyphyll	Frond of juvenile ferns of the genera *Teratophyllum, Lomagramma* and *Lomariopsis*.
bifurcate	To fork or divide into two parts or branches.
bipinnate	Twice pinnate, the final divisions being termed pinnules.
bryophytes	Mosses and liverworts.
buttress root	A root that grows from the stem of a tree, giving support to the trunk.
callus	Proliferation of cells from a piece of tissue under aseptic conditions.
crosier	The coiled young frond of the fern; the fiddlehead.
cultivar	A cultivated subdivision of the species.
diaphoretic	Relating to or causing perspiration.
dimorphism	Two morphological forms in a single species. In leaf dimorphism, two forms of leaves are present in the same plant.
diuretic	A drug that increases the flow of urine.
epiphyte	Plants that grow on other plants.
explant	A piece of tissue used to induce callus in tissue culture.
fossil	The preserved remains of organisms from a very long time ago.
frond	The leaf of a fern.
genus	A group of closely related species with a number of obvious common characteristics. (plural: genera)
indusium	The flap covering the group of sporangia in a fern. (plural: indusia)
lamina	The flat part of a frond.
microphyll	The small, sterile leaves of fern allies.
mutation	A permanent genetic change in a characteristic of an organism.

palmate frond	The frond is divided into lobes arranged like the fingers on a palm.
phloem	Food-conducting tissue of plants.
pinna	The leaflet of a pinnate frond. (plural: pinnae)
pinnate frond	The frond is divided into distinct divisions, the pinnae and these are arranged along the extension of the stalk.
pinnule	The ultimate leaflet of a bipinnate frond.
prothallus	The small, flattened structure arising by the germination of a spore and bearing male and female sex organs. (plural: prothalli)
pup	A common term for a young fern developing from the nest of a Staghorn.
rachis	The axis bearing the pinnae of a pinnate frond.
rhizoid	A filamentous, root-like structure of the prothallus.
rhizome	A long and slender creeping stem of a fern.
rootstock	The short stem of a fern, which can be either erect or horizontal.
serrate	Like the edge of a saw.
simple frond	Frond whose blade is not dissected into pinnae.
sinus	The gap between two lobes of a frond, pinna or pinnule.
sorus	A group of sporangia. (plural: sori)
sp.	Short form for species. (plural: spp.)
species	A group of organisms that interbreed with each other to give fertile offsprings. (plural: species)
sporangium	The club-shaped spore case of a fern borne of a stalk. (plural: sporangia)
spore	The microscopic reproductive unit of a fern.
sporeling	The young of a fern.
sporocarp	A spore producing structure of water ferns consisting of a sorus completely enclosed by the indusium.
stipe	The stalk of a frond.
stomium	The point of weakness where the sporangium splits open.
systematist	A person who studies the identification and classification of organisms.
trifoliate	Fronds with three pinnae.
tripinnate	Three times pinnate, the final divisions being termed pinnules.
tri-radiate	Having three rays or radiating branches.
vascular strands	Conducting tubes found within the stems and fronds of ferns made of xylem and phloem.
vermiculite	Material used in heat and sound insulation, consisting mainly of hydrated silicate of magnesium, aluminum and iron. Popularly used as a rooting medium for plants.
xylem	Water-conducting tissue of plants.

BIBLIOGRAPHY

CAMUS, J.M., A.C. JERMY & B.A. THOMAS (1991). *A world of ferns*. Natural History Museum, London.

CROFT, J.R. (1982). *Ferns and man in New Guinea*. Paper presented to the Papua New Guinea Botany Society.

DUNK, Gillean (1986). *Ferns for the home and garden*. Angus & Robertson, London.

DUNBAR, Lin (1989). *Ferns of the coastal plain*. University of South Carolina Press.

EDIE, H.H. (1978). *Ferns of Hong Kong*. Hong Kong University Press.

EVANS, I.A. & J. MASON (1965). Carcinogenic activity of Bracken. *Nature* 208: 913-914.

FLETCHER, W.W. & KIRKWOOD, R.C. (1979). The bracken fern (*Pteridium aquilinum*) L. (Kuhn); its biology and control. In: Dyer, A. F. (ed.) *The experimental biology of ferns*. Academic Press, London, New York and San Francisco. pp. 591–636.

GIMLETTE, John D. (1981). *Malay poisons and charm cures*. Kuala Lumpur: Oxford University Press.

GOUDEY, C.J. (1988). *A handbook of ferns for Australia and New Zealand*. Lothian, Melbourne, Sydney and Auckland.

HIRONO, I., C. SHIBUYA, M. SHIMIZU & K. FUSHIMI (1972). Carcinogenic activity of processed Bracken used as human food. *Journal of the National Cancer Institute*, 48: 1245–1250.

HODGE, W.H. (1973). Fern foods of Japan and the problem of toxicity. *American Fern Journal*, 63: 77–80.

HOLTTUM, R.E. (1938). The ecology of tropical pteridophytes. In: Fr. Verdoorn (ed.) *Manual of Pteridology*. Martinus Nijhoff, The Hague. pp. 420–450.

HOLTTUM, R.E. (1986). A revised flora of Malaya. *Vol. II Ferns of Malaya*. Government Printing Office, Singapore.

HOLTTUM, R.E. (1988). Ferns. In: Earl of Cranbrook (ed.) *Key Environments — Malaysia*. IUCN & Pergamon Press, Oxford. pp. 77–87.

JONES, David L. (1987). *Encyclopaedia of ferns*. London: British Museum (Natural History).

MICKEL, John (1979). *The home gardener's book of ferns*. Holt, Rinehart and Winston, New York.

PADHYA, M.A. & A.R. MEHTA (1982). Propagation of fern (*Nephrolepis*) through tissue culture. *Plant Cell Reports*, 1: 261–263.

PAGE, C. N. (1979). The diversity of ferns - an ecological perspective. In: A. F. Dyer (ed.) *The Experimental Biology of Ferns*. Academic Press, London, New York and San Francisco. pp. 9–56.

PAGE, C. N. (1988). *Ferns—their habitats in the British and Irish landscape*. Collins, London.

PAMUKCU, A.M. & J.M. PRICE (1969). Induction of intestinal and urinary bladder cancer in rats by feeding bracken fern. Journal of the National Cancer Institute, 43: 275–281.

PARRIS, B.S., R.S. BEAMAN & J. H. BEAMAN (1992). *The plants of Mount Kinabalu. I. Ferns and fern allies*. Royal Botanic Gardens, Kew.

VERDOORN, Fr. (ed.) (1938). *Manual of Pteridology*. Martinus Nijhoff, The Hague.

WEE Y.C. (1984). *Common ferns and fern-allies of Singapore*. Malayan Nature Society, Singapore.

WEE Y.C. (1979). The development of plantlets from strobilus branches in *Lycopodium phlegmaria*. American Fern Journal, 69: 80–82.

WEE Y.C. (1992). *A guide to the ferns of Singapore*. Singapore Science Centre.

WEE Y.C., S.H. Kwa & C.S. Loh (1992). Production of sporophytes from *Platycerium coronarium* and *P. ridleyi* frond strips and rhizome pieces cultured in vitro. *American Fern Journal*, 82: 75–79.

WEE Y.C., R.K. SENTHIL-POONKODI & B.L. ONG (1992). Frond-bud propagation of *Asplenium nidus. Journal of Horticultural Science.* 67: 813–815.

WINSTEDT, Richard (1961). *The Malay magician, being shaman, saiva and sufi*. Routledge & Kegan Paul, London.

ZAMORA, P.M. & L. CO (1986). Economic ferns. In: *Guide to Philippine flora and fauna Vol. II.* pp. 1-72. Natural Resources Management Centre, Ministry of Natural Resources and University of the Philippines.

FERN SOCIETIES

Australia

Fern Society of South Australia Inc., GPO Box 711, Adelaide, South Australia 5001.

Fern Society of Victoria Inc., PO Box 45, Heidelberg, Victoria 3081.

Fern Study Group of the Society for Growing Australian Plants, c/o Mr Peter Hind, 41 Miller Street, Mt. Druitt, New South Wales 2226.
[e-mail: peterh@rbgsyd.gov.au – home page: http://www.ozemail.com.au/~sgap/]

Sunshine Coast Fern Society, PO Box 47, Woombye, Queensland 4559.

Tasmanian Fern Society, c/o Julie Haas, 72 Bush Creek Road, Lenah Valley, Tasmania 7008.

Western Australian Fern Society, c/o Mrs J. Friend, 210 Kent Street, Rockingham, Western Australia 6168.

China

The Fern Society of China, c/o Prof. K.H. Shing, Institute of Botany, Academia Sinica, Beijing 100044.

India

Indian Fern Society, c/o Prof. S.S. Bir, Department of Botany, Punjab University, Patiala 147 002

Japan

Japanese Pteridological Society, Botanical Gardens, University of Tokyo, Hakusan 3-7-1, Bunkyo-ku, Tokyo 112.

Nippon Fernist Club, c/o Institute of Forest Botany, Faculty of Agriculture, University of Tokyo, Hongo, Bunkyo-ku, Tokyo 113

Malaysia

No formal fern society, but there is the possibility of a future fern group forming in the Malayan Nature Society, PO Box 10750, 50724 Kuala Lumpur.
[e-mail: mns@natsoc.po.my – home page: http://www.charity.org.my/msia_nature_soc]

Netherlands

Nederlandse Varenvereniging, c/o Jan G. Greep, V. Remagenlaan 17, 6824 LX Arnhem.

New Zealand

Nelson Fern Society Inc. of New Zealand, c/o Mrs J. Bonnington, 9 Bay View Road, Atawhai, Nelson.

Waikato Fern Club, c/o Mrs Eila McKenzie, 164 Upper Dinsdale Road, Hamilton.

Philippines

Fern Society of the Philippines, c/o National Museum, P. Burgos Street, Manila.

Singapore

No formal fern society, but there is the possibility of a future fern group forming in the Nature Society (Singapore), 601 Sims Drive #04-04, Pan-I Complex, Singapore 387382. [e-mail: natsoc@mbox2.singnet.com.sg – home page: http://rs.nic.net.sg/virtuoucity/nss/index.html]

South Africa

Fern Society of Southern Africa, PO Box 11260, Brooklyn 0011, Transvaal.

Switzerland

Schweizerische Vereiningung der Farnfreunde, c/o Dr J.J. Schneller, Institüt für Systematische Botanik, Zollikerstrasse 107, CH-8008, Zürich.

United Kingdom

The British Pteridological Society, c/o Miss A.M. Paul, Department of Botany, The National History Museum, Cromwell Road, London SW7 5BD. [e-mail: amp@nhm.ac.uk]

United States of America

American Fern Society, c/o Dr W.C. Taylor, Botany Department, Milwaukee Public Museum, 800 W Wells Street, Milwaukee, Wisconsin 53233-1478.
[home page: http://www.visuallink.net/fern]

Birmingham Fern Society, c/o Mrs R. E. Smith, 4736 7th Avenue South, Birmingham, Alabama 35222.

Corpus Christi Fern Society, c/o P. Coleman, 438 Claremont Street, Corpus Christi, Texas 78412.

Delaware Valley Fern and Wildflower Society, c/o Mrs C.W. Bondinell, 1512 Franklin Lane, Wayne, Pennsylvania 19087.

Fern Study Group of the Northwest Horticultural Society, c/o Mr N. Hall, 1230 North East 88th Street, Seattle, Washington 98115.

Hardy Fern Foundation, c/o Barbara Carman, PO Box 166, Medina, Washington 98036-0166. [e-mail: sueman@darkwing.uoregon.edu – home page: http://darkwing.uoregon.edu/~sueman/]

International Tropical Fern Society, c/o 14895 Gardenhill Drive, La Mirada, California 90638.

Los Angeles International Fern Society, PO Box 90943, Pasadena, California 91109-0943.

Louisiana Fern Society, c/o Mary Elliott, 41038 S. Range Road, Ponchatoula, Louisiana 70454. [e-mail: 75103,1016@compuserve.com]

Memphis Fern Society, c/o Chris Spindel, 3985 South Galloway Drive, Memphis, Tennessee 38111-6841. [e-mail: fyrnlady@aol.com]

New York Fern Society, c/o Dr John Mickel, New York Botanic Garden, Bronx, New York 10458.

San Diego Fern Society, 1418 Park Row La Jolla, California 92037-3710. [e-mail: sdfern@inetworld.net – home page: http://www.inetworld.net/~sdfern/society.htm]

San Francisco Fern Society, 4726 Hilltop Drive, El Sobrante, California 94803.

South Florida Fern Society, c/o John Corrigan, Fairchild Tropical Garden, 10901 Old Cutler Road, Miami, Florida 33156.

Southwestern Fern Society, c/o Ann Herrington, 2121 Richwood Drive, Garland, Texas 75228. [e-mail: annh@airmail.net]

Tampa Bay Fern Club, c/o Carl Strohmenger, PO Box 15578, Tampa, Florida 33684-5578. [e-mail: cstrohme@com.1.med.usf.edu]

West Florida Fern Society, c/o Dr M. Cousens, Department of Biology, University of West Florida, Pensacola, Florida 32504.

ACKNOWLEDGEMENTS

Most of the photographs in this book were taken during the last 20 years when I was associated with the Department of Botany (now the School of Biological Sciences), National University of Singapore. It was during the annual Botany Honours field trips that I had the opportunity to observe ferns and photograph them in their natural habitats. My sincere thanks to Dr A.N. Rao, then Professor of Botany, for allowing me to participate in these trips; to Dr Hsuan Keng for his leadership in the field; to the colleagues who helped on these trips; and to the annual cohorts of Botany Honours students who provided companionship in the field and made the trips fun and memorable. Last but not least, I wish to record my thanks to my editor, Ms Harlinah Whyte, who so skilfully polished and organised my raw manuscript and colour slides into the book that you have before you.

A number of photographs have been provided by past students: Ms Yeo Hwee Yng (p. 23, bottom right), Ms Sreedharan Shylaja (p. 56), Ms Latifah bt. Md. Hussain (p. 23 top right and p. 147, top) and Dr Kwa Siew Hwa (p. 63). The photographs on the cover and on pages 4, 9 and 66 are by Luca Tettoni.

INDEX

A

acrophyll, 175
Acrostichum, 67, 84
  Acrostichum aureum (Mangrove Fern,
  Swamp Fern), 41, 45, 88
  Acrostichum speciosum (Mangrove Fern,
  Swamp Fern), 88
Adder's-tongue Fern, 19, 34, 35, 36, 45, 62,
  146, 147. See also *Ophioglossum.*
Adiantum (Maidenhair), 7, 20, 36, 46, 47, 67, 73
  Adiantum capillus-veneris (Venus-hair
  Fern, European Maidenhair), 9, 35, 45, 46
  Adiantum capillus-veneris cv. Fimbriatum, 9
  Adiantum capillus-veneris cv. Mairisii, 9
  Adiantum caudatum, 91
  Adiantum cuneatum, 9
  Adiantum flabellulatum, 46
  Adiantum latifolium, 91
  Adiantum macrophyllum, 46
  Adiantum pedatum, 45, 50
  Adiantum peruvianum, 68
Aglaomorpha, 77
  Aglaomorpha heraclea, 92–93
Anabaena azollae (algae), 46, 101
Angiopteris, 41, 45, 58, 67
  Angiopteris evecta (Elephant Fern), 42, 46,
  58, 92–93
Angsana (*Pterocarpus indicus*), 84
annulus, 20
antheridia, 25, 26
Antrophyum, 77
  Antrophyum latifolium, 75
archegonia, 25, 26
Arcosorus, 77
Asplenium (Spleenwort), 36
  Asplenium batuense, 60
  Asplenium longissimum, 60, 95
  Asplenium macrophyllum, 95
  Asplenium nidus (Bird's-nest Fern), 19, 47,
  59, 61, 70, 73, 76, 81, 85, 97–98
  Asplenium nidus var. *plicatum* (Lasagne
  Fern), 70
  Asplenium tenerum, 60, 61, 75
  Asplenium trichomanes, 45
Athyrium, 73
auricles, 58
Avicennia, 83

Azolla (Water Fern), 26, 83
  Azolla pinnata (Mosquito Fern), 46, 101

B

bathyphylls, 175
Belvesia, 77
  Belvisia revoluta, 103
  beverages, 44–45
Bird's-nest Fern, 19, 36, 47, 59, 60, 70, 73, 85,
  97–98, 100, 114, 123, 142, 146, 167, 176.
  See also *Asplenium nidus.*
Blechnum (Blechnum Fern), 73
  Blechnum indicum, 41
  Blechnum orientale (Centipede Fern, *paku
  lipan*), 14, 41, 42, 45, 46, 79, 103
Bolbitis appendiculata, 75, 105
Bolbitis heteroclita, 105
Boston Fern, 7
Botrychium (Moonwort), 36
  Botrychium lunaria (Moonwort), 35
Bracken Fern, 7, 34, 43, 44, 46, 51, 158, 159.
  See also *Pteridium.*
Brake. See *Pteris.*
Broad-leafed Mahogany (*Swietenia
  macrophylla*), 84
Brugeria, 83
bryophyte, 73, 75, 81, 154
bulbil, 60, 61

C

Calymmodon, 77
Campnosperma auriculatum (*terentang*), 33
Centipede Fern, 14, 41, 42, 103
Ceratopteris thalictroides (Horned Fern, *sayur
  kodok*), 42, 83
Cheilanthes tenuifolia (Lip Fern), 106, 107
Cheiropleuria bicuspis, 106, 107
Chinese Lace Fern, 171
Cibotium (Tree Fern), 76
  Cibotium barometz (Golden Chicken Fern),
  34, 50, 77, 107
classification of ferns, 8
Climbing Fern, 7, 41, 50. See also *Lygodium.*
Clubmoss, 7, 29, 51, 137. See also *Lycopodium.*
coal, 7
Colysis pedunculata, 109
crosier, 13, 14, 56

Crypsinus, 77
    Crypsinus wrayi, 109
Ctenopteris, 77
    Ctenopteris obliquata, 111
cultivars, 8
Cyathea (Tree Fern), 7, 41, 50, 76
    Cyathea contaminans (Tree Fern), 41, 42, 76, 111
    Cyathea latebrosa (Tree Fern), 18, 112
    Cyathea mannjana (Tree Fern), 45
    Cyathea moluccana, 112
Cyclosorus, 71

D

Davallia, 46, 63
    Davallia denticulata (Rabbit's-foot Fern), 18, 114
    Davallia triphylla, 76, 116, 117
Dicksonia (Tree Fern), 50
    Dicksonia squarrosa (Tree Fern), 46
Dicranopteris (resam), 7, 46, 67, 79, 117–118, 127
    Dicranopteris curranii (resam), 50, 117
    Dicranopteris linearis (resam), 23, 46, 47, 50, 117
    Dicranopteris linearis var. *subpectinata*, 118
Didymochlaena, 13
Diplazium esculentum, 41
Dipteris, 119
    Dipteris conjugata, 14, 119–120
    Dipteris lobbiana, 73, 120
Disc Staghorn Fern, 33, 36, 39, 48, 81, 85, 153–154, 156. See also *Platycerium coronarium*.
Dischidia nummularia, 142
diseases, 69–70
Doryopteris ludens, 120
Dragon's-scale Fern, 85, 154, 164, 167. See also *Pyrrosia piloselloides*.
Drynaria (Oak-leaf Fern), 47, 85
    Drynaria quercifolia (Oak-leaf Fern), 45, 123, 125
    Drynaria rigidula (Oak-leaf Fern), 45, 77, 127
    Drynaria sparsisora (Oak-leaf Fern), 45, 123
Dryopteris (Spear Fern), 46
    Dryopteris cristata, 45
    Dryopteris filix-mas (Male Fern), 35, 39, 42, 44, 45
    Dryopteris marginalis (Marginal Fern), 45

E

ekor merak, 29
Egenolfia appendiculata. See *Bolbitis appendiculata.*
Elaphoglossum (Stag's-tongue Fern), 77
Elephant Fern, 42, 58, 92. See also *Angiopteris*.

Elkhorn Fern, 48, 58, 59. See also *Platycerium*.
epiphytes, 7, 73, 75, 77, 79, 81, 84
Equisetum (Horsetail), 29, 39
    Equisetum arvense (Horsetail), 42, 45, 51
    Equisetum debile, 51
    Equisetum giganteum (Giant Horsetail), 45
    Equisetum hyemale, 46, 51
erosion control, 46
European Maidenhair Fern. See *Adiantum capillus-veneris.*

F

fern allies, 29–31
fern societies, 55, 182–184
fertiliser, 46, 69
Filmy Fern, 75, 81, 130. See also *Hymenophyllum* and *Trichomanes.*
folklore, 34–39
food, 41–44
fronds, 7, 13–14

G

Giant Horsetail, 7, 45
Gleichenia, 7, 46, 67, 79, 120, 145
    Gleichenia truncata, 127
Gold Fern, 13
Golden Chicken Fern, 34, 50, 77, 107
Goniophlebium percussum, 18, 81, 128
Grammitis, 77
Grass Fern, 36, 81, 171

H

habitats:
    agricultural areas, 81
    lowland rainforest, 73–76
    mountain forest, 76–79
    secondary forest, 79
    swamps and open waters, 83–84
    urban areas, 84
Hanging Adder's-tongue Fern, 39, 146. See also *Ophioglossum.*
Helminthostachys zeylanica (tunjuk langit), 42
Heterogonium sagenoides, 128
Histiopteris stipulacea, 130
Holttum, R.E., 107
Holttum's Staghorn Fern, 154
Horned Fern, 42
Horsetail, 7, 29, 33, 39, 42, 45, 46, 51. See also *Equisetum.*
Humata (Squirrel's-foot Fern), 77
    Humata angustata, 76
Hymenophyllum (Filmy Ferns), 77, 130, 132
    Hymenophyllum serrulatum, 130

I
indusium, 20

J
jambu merak, 29

L
Ladder Fern, 41, 47
lamina, 13
Lasagne Fern, 70
Lecanopteris carnosa, 46, 77, 132
Lecanopteris sinuosa, 134, 135
Lepisorus, 8
life cycle of a fern, 24–27
Lindsaea, 73
   Lindsaea doryphora, 73
   Lindsaea ensifolia, 135, 159
   Lindsaea lucida, 73
   Lindsaea nitida, 73
   Lindsaea parasitica, 75, 137
   Lindsaea repens, 75
   Lindsaea rigida, 137
Lip Fern, 106
liverworts, 7, 76
Lomagramma, 75
Lomariopsis, 75
Lycopodium (Clubmoss), 29, 51, 77, 137
   Lycopodium cernuum (Nodding
   Clubmoss), 29, 79
   Lycopodium clavatum, 46
   Lycopodium macrophyllum, 46
   Lycopodium phlegmaria (Tassel Fern), 62
   Lycopodium selago, 45
Lygodium (Climbing Fern), 7, 50, 52, 79
   Lygodium flexuosum, 85, 139
   Lygodium microphyllum, 50, 85
   Lygodium salicifolium, 50

M
Maidenhair Fern, 7, 9, 35, 36, 45, 47, 50, 58,
   67, 68, 91. See also *Adiantum*.
Male Fern, 35, 39, 42, 44, 45
Mangrove Fern. See *Acrostichum*.
Marattia, 41, 58
Marginal Fern, 45
Marsilea (Water Clover), 26, 41
   Marsilea crenata (Water Clover, Water
   Shamrock, *tapak itek*), 83, 139
Matonia pectinata, 141
Matteuccia struthiopteris (Ostrich Fern), 42, 44
medicine, 45–46
Merinthosorus, 77
Mesophlebion chlamydophorum, 141
Mexican Lilac (*Glircidia sepium*), 84

Microlepia, 73
   Microlepia speluncae, 141
microphylls, 29
Microsorum punctatum, 46, 142
Monogramma trichoidea, 75
Moonwort, 35, 36
Mosquito Fern, 46, 101
moss, 7, 76

N
Nephrolepis (Boston Fern, Ladder Fern,
   Sword Fern), 7, 46, 47, 61, 63
   Nephrolepis acutifolia, 81, 142
   Nephrolepis biserrata, 20, 79, 83, 85, 142,
   145, 152
   Nephrolepis cordifolia (Sword Fern), 42, 46,
   61
   Nephrolepis hirsurula, 41
Nodding Clubmoss. See *Lycopodium cernuum*.

O
Oak-leaf Fern, 85, 123, 125, 127. See also
   Drynaria.
Oleandra pistillaris, 145
Ophioglossum (Adder's-tongue Fern), 17, 34,
   45, 62
   Ophioglossum nudicaule (Adder's-tongue
   Fern), 23, 36
   Ophioglossum pendulum (Hanging
   Adder's-tongue Fern), 36, 39, 146
   Ophioglossum reticulatum (Adder's-tongue
   Fern), 147
   Ophioglossum vulgatum, 35
Osmunda regalis (Royal Fern), 42
Ostrich Fern, 42, 44

P
paku langsuyur, 36
paku lipan, 103
paku merak, 29
paku wangi, 150
pests, 69–70
phloem, 11
Photinopteris speciosa, 149
Phymatodes sinuosa. See *Lecanopteris sinuosa*.
Phymatopteris triloba, 149
Phymatosorus scolopendria (*paku wangi*), 11, 81,
   150
Pigeon Orchid (*Dendrobium crumenatum*), 150
pinna, 14
pinnule, 14
Pityrogramma austroamericana (Gold Fern), 12
Pityrogramma calomelanos (Silver Fern), 12, 17,
   22, 46, 51, 85, 152

plantlet, 59–61
Platycerium (Staghorn Fern), 7, 8, 14, 19, 46, 63
   Platycerium bifurcatum (Elkhorn Fern), 48, 55, 58
   Platycerium bifurcatum var. *willinckii* (Elkhorn Fern), 48
   Platycerium coronarium (Disc Staghorn), 17, 36, 48, 63, 76, 81, 85, 153–154
   Platycerium holttumi (Holttum's Staghorn), 154
   Platycerium platylobium, 76
   Platycerium ridleyi (Ridley's Staghorn), 48, 52, 65, 156
   Platycerium wallichii, 76
   Platycerium wandae, 47
polypodium, 63
Polystichum linearis, 51
Pronephrium, 73
   Pronephrium salicifolium, 60
   Pronephrium triphyllum, 81, 156
prothallus, 25, 26, 56, 73
Psilotum nudum (Whisk Fern), 29, 46
Pteridium (Bracken Fern), 42, 44, 46, 79
   Pteridium aquilinum (Bracken Fern), 7, 34, 45, 158, 159
   Pteridium caudatum (Bracken Fern), 34
Pteris (Brake), 46, 73
   Pteris ensiformis, 46, 158, 159, 161
   Pteris ensiformis var. *Victoriae*, 159, 161
   Pteris multifida, 41
   Pteris vittata, 22, 85, 161
pup, 55, 58
Pyrrosia, 8
   Pyrrosia floccigera, 163
   Pyrrosia lanceolata, 73, 163
   Pyrrosia longifolia, 73, 81, 163, 164
   Pyrrosia piloselloides (Dragon's-scale Fern), 23, 81, 85, 163, 164, 166

Q
Quercifilix zeylanica, 168

R
Rabbit's-foot Fern, 114, 116
Rain Tree (*Samanea saman*), 73, 84, 123, 150, 154, 176
resam, 7, 50. See also *Dicranopteris*.
rhizoid, 25
rhizome, 11, 25, 29, 42, 58
Rhizophora, 83
Ridley's Staghorn, 48, 52, 156. See also *Platycerium ridleyi*.
roots, 19, 58, 62
rootstock, 11

Royal Fern, 42
rumah langsuyur, 36
runner, 61

S
Sadleria, 50
Salvinia (Water Spangle), 26, 83
   Salvinia molesta (Water Spangle), 168
sayur kodok, 42
Schizaea dichotoma (Grass Fern), 171
Schizaea digitata (Grass Fern), 36, 39, 41
Scleroglossum, 77
Sea Almond (*Terminalia catappa*), 84
Sea Apple (*Eugenia grandis*), 84
Selaginella (Spikemoss, *paku merak, jambu merak, ekor merak*), 29
   Selaginella involvens, 45
semun bidadari, 36
Shoestring Fern, 176, 177. See also *Vittaria*.
Silver Fern, 13, 85, 152. See also *Pityrogramma calomelanos*.
soil, 68
sorus, 20
Spear Fern. See *Dryopteris*.
Sphaerostephanos, 20
Sphenomeris chinensis (Chinese Lace Fern), 171
Spider Brake, 41
Spikemoss, 29, 45
Spleenwort, 36
sporangium, 7, 19–22, 29, 55
spore, 7, 22, 23, 25, 26, 33, 55, 56
spore culture, 55–56
sporeling, 25, 26, 56
sport, 8
Squirrel's-foot Fern. See *Humata*.
Staghorn Fern, 7, 8, 14, 19, 36, 46, 58, 76, 114, 123, 146. See also *Platycerium*.
Stenochlaena palustris (Climbing Fern), 17, 18, 41, 50, 83, 172
stipe, 13
stomium, 20
Strangling Fig (*Ficus* sp.), 73, 85, 176
Swamp Fern, 41, 88. See also *Acrostichum*.
Sword Fern. See *Nephrolepis*.

T
Taenitis blechnoides, 172
Taenitis dimorpha, 172
Taenitis interrupta, 73
tapak itek, 139
Tassel Fern, 62
Tectaria, 73
   Tectaria singaporeana, 17, 73, 174

Teratophyllum, 75
    Teratophyllum aculeatum, 175
tetrad, 23
tissue culture, 63–65
Tree Fern, 7, 41, 47, 48, 50, 51, 52, 76, 77, 107,
    111–112. See also *Cibotium, Cyathea* and
    Dicksonia.
Trichomanes (Filmy Fern), 77, 130, 132
tunjuk langit, 42

V

vegetative propagation, 58–62
Venus-hair Fern. See *Adiantum capillus-*
    veneris.
Vittaria elongata (Shoestring Fern), 176
Vittaria ensiformis (Shoestring Fern), 83, 177

W

Water Clover, 139. See also *Marsilea.*
Water Shamrock, 139. See also *Marsilea.*
Water Spangle, 168. See also *Salvinia.*
Whisk Fern, 29

X

Xiphopteris, 77
xylem, 11

Y

Yellow Flame Tree (*Peltophorum pterocarpum*),
    167